THE MOST SUCCESSFUL FAILURE IN THE WORLD

Building a Business that Gives Life Meaning

JEFF HASTINGS

ChartHousePress.com

The Most Successful Failure in the World

By Jeffrey L. Hastings

© 2015 by the Jeff Hastings Agency, Inc.

ISBN-13: 978-0-63125-052-1
Chart House Press, LLC.
24044 Cinco Village Blvd. Ste. 100
Katy, TX 77494   281-752-6565
www.ChartHousePress.com

Jeff@JeffHastingsAgency.com
JeffHastingsAgency.com
www.twitter.com/JHastingsAgency
http://www.linkedin.com/in/JeffLHastings

Edited by: Carly Drake and Ella Herrean
Cover Design by Ida Jansson
Book Design by Megan LaFollett
Illustrations by: J. Eric Dunlap

To every lost entrepreneur and dreamer

who is looking for a better way.

CONTENTS

"Your work is going to fill a large part of your life, and the only way to be truly satisfied is to do what you believe is great work. And the only way to do great work is to love what you do. If you haven't found it yet, keep looking. Don't settle. As with all matters of the heart, you'll know when you find it. And, like any great relationship, it just gets better and better as the years roll on. So keep looking until you find it. Don't settle."

Steve Jobs
(1955 – 2011)

PROLOGUE

Starting and owning your own business is as much a part of the American spirit as baseball and apple pie. This country was colonized on the principle of breaking away from the status quo to find happiness in freedom, and many believe that entrepreneurship is their path to that better quality of life and happiness. However, during the journey to this life of financial freedom and success, many people lose what they hold dear but often take for granted. Their health, well-being, and important relationships to name a few. And while some people are fortunate enough to see the decay in their lives before it's too late and have time to save it; others, like the story I'm about to tell you, are not quite so lucky.

The events that transpire in this tale center around a man named Alex Moss. As the CEO and founder of Moss Global he lived a life of privileged decadence. His company was one of the largest internet marketing firms in the country and as such he owned many of the toys most inspiring entrepreneurs dream of - a private jet, a yacht, several extravagant homes, and nearly every gadget you could think of. He was on a first name basis with fellow billionaires and political heavies, and seemed to have a new super model on his arm at every event. Dedicated to the lifestyle and leading by example, he worked hard and played hard. He always received the maximum allowance at casinos, could be found slicing through the mountains as the most exclusive ski resorts, and floating upon the sun dappled blue waters of the Mediterranean in what he considered to be his pride and joy – his 85' custom sailing yacht. When people asked him when he would sleep, his favorite response was, "I'll sleep when I'm dead." He never gave much thought to such careless clichéd phrases until six months before his fiftieth birthday.

After much research and many interviews, I am able to start his story for you at the onset of that fateful revelation.

PART 1
DISCOVERING LIFE'S PURPOSE

"Sometimes in tragedy, we find our life's true purpose."

Robert Brault
Author

The dove grey car rolled to a near silent stop along the curb. Joggers and cyclists alike barely turned their heads to notice the luxury vehicle with the familiar statuette on the hood. This was Chelsea, after all, and a Rolls Royce Phantom was nothing exciting. Even when the chauffeur stepped out to open the door, hardly a glance was spared for the man who emerged.

This is what Alex Moss liked about New York, and why he had made it his home for the past twenty years. It was easy to go unnoticed, until you wanted the attention. As the founder of one of the largest internet startups in the country, anonymity always meant he got more done.

"Will you be needing the umbrella today, sir? Those clouds look a bit sketchy." With a glare at the darkening sky, the chauffeur was already reaching for the umbrella that he had extracted from the car's door.

"That won't be necessary, Tony, but thank you." Alex clasped the last button on his black cashmere pea coat before patting the chauffeur on the shoulder. "Why don't you go find yourself a cup of coffee, and work on your sketches, hmm? I have a feeling the clouds will break and the sunrise over the Hudson is going to be gorgeous today. When I get back I would like to see what you've done."

"Ummm, o-ok, yeah, sure. Thank you Mr. Moss." Anthony hesitated before he asked and was taken back when Alex had called him Tony. "Uh, Mr. Moss...is everything alright?"

"Everything's great," Alex insisted.

Anthony smiled timidly before nodding and sliding back into the shiny grey Rolls before he pulled away into the early morning traffic. Alex rubbed his chin as he wondered why his positive outlook on the day took his tenured chauffeur by surprise. Were his remarks that much out of the ordinary? Maybe the clapping on the shoulder was a bit much. Alex was never usually one to be so cordial with his staff, but things were different now. Taking an interest in the dreams of his friends and acquaintances was something Alex had always wished he had made the time to do. But, like most of his personal interests, this was just another one on the long checklist of regrets that was put aside for the pursuit of a dream. Or at least what he thought was his dream.

Popping the lid on his paper coffee cup, Alex blew on the steaming liquid as he headed towards the pier off of West 15th Street and Eleventh Avenue. The rich aroma of the warm brew filled his senses and he marveled at how coffee could smell completely different than how it tasted. He smirked, shaking his head as he reached the old and familiar bannister that ran along the pier. This place used to be where Alex would come when his life got out of hand and he needed to clear his mind to think. But for some reason, he just stopped coming. That's how life is though, isn't it? We get so caught up in the game it often takes a tragedy to knock us down and bring us to our knees to realize what really matters. And to most New Yorkers, the empty skyline of where the Twin Towers used to stand is a constant reminder of how precious life really is. Alex knew he could have very easily been a victim on 9/11. He passed by the massive buildings on a regular basis many times without giving them a second look. He took those towers for granted thinking they'd always be there to admire. Even the gleaming newly erected One World Trade Center building held a powerful reminder.

Alex stared at the waves lapping against the pier wall beneath him, allowing their hypnotic rhythm to lull him into a trance as he relaxed his gaze and reflected. Alex usually didn't allow his mind to concentrate on much more than the upkeep of his business. But as he sipped on his full roast coffee and gazed down at the murky water, he couldn't think of a better time than now to allow his mind to be immersed in the present and have freedom to roam.

Of course as expected, the thoughts he was trying so desperately to escape came rushing into his memory. It had only been a few weeks ago, but the event was traumatic and he knew his life would never be the same. But then again, it was finally clear to him that he was on the wrong path and an event such as this was the only way the "man upstairs" could get his attention. That is how Alex referred to God and communicated his belief to others. But now, things were different and he knew there must be a higher being.

It all happened in Detroit at one of the most important meetings Alex had ever attended. He had attended meetings like this one before, but this year was different. He had an opportunity in front of him that could catapult his company into one of the leading internet marketing companies in the world, not just in the United States. The city and the automotive industry were struggling to regain their status and they needed the services of his company to do so. Every major US automobile maker was represented including a handful of State Representatives and Congressmen.

As the group finished their applause and the MC started to introduce the next speaker, Alex's hands began to sweat and his heart pounded with nervous excitement. He usually didn't feel this flushed before he addressed an audience but knew this was the moment he had been waiting for. He knew that all of his hard work, sacrifice and dedication came down to this defining moment.

Like a cheetah on the hunt, Alex thrived on the huge adrenaline rush that public speaking provided. These deals and contracts were what he had dedicated his entire life to. Although he sacrificed a great deal of his personal life, Alex didn't see it as such. To him it was a requirement in order to pave a road of success inwhich most people only dreamt about. His family rarely saw him and his friends were merely business acquaintances. He couldn't remember the last time he had been to any meaningful personal event, but these conferences, they were what made him feel alive.

Alex stood off to the side of the stage and gave the audience one last glance. He went over his presentation in his mind trying not to forget important facts about each member in the audience. As his thoughts skimmed over the last details, the speaker announced his name. Alex took a step and winced. The pain in his side that he had been ignoring for months decided that now was the perfect time to grow from an irritating ache to a sharp pain. The audience started their applause when they noticed Alex walk slowly to the podium. The pain grew with every step and was slowly shooting up to his chest. He tried to school his features into a more relaxed state, and hoped no one could guess at his pain. The room began to spin as he stretched out his hand to greet the MC. After the gentleman let go and patted him on the back, Alex swallowed thickly, wondering if the slipperiness of his sweaty palm was as bad as he feared. The audience sat in quiet anticipation as Alex adjusted his tie knot, sticking the tip of his index finger in the space between his collar and neck. He knew they were waiting for him to begin, but his mouth felt as though it were full of cotton. Eying the glass of water left for him at the stand he reached for it. No sooner had his fingers curled around the cool glass, his knees gave out and he collapsed. That was the last thing he remembered.

Somewhere between Woodward Avenue and the Detroit Medical Center, Alex woke to the sound of screaming sirens, a pounding headache and voices frantically speaking over him. His eyelids felt heavy and giving into their weight he let them close. The next time they opened it was to a new nightmare of the doctor, the questions, and the scans. But, worst of all, he remembered the news. It was the one detail his mind played over and over, still in disbelief that it had happened. Even more so, that it had happened to him.

Trying to force the horrible thought back into his box of unpleasant memories, he closed his eyes and felt the cool breeze ruffle his hair. The gulls cried overhead, and he tried to imagine himself on a tropical beach instead. He was daydreaming of white sands, blue water and tan skin when he heard a throat clear behind him. Alex opened his eyes with a smile that quickly turned sour at the sight of the grey waters of the Hudson River. The throat clearer turned out to be his Director of Customer Relations, Peter Walker.

Peter had his own cup of coffee and the two old friends stood shoulder to shoulder, sharing a moment of silence as they sipped from their cups. Even though they hadn't spent a lot of time together over the past few years, their friendship had stood the course of time. Words were not always necessary to understand one another and even when they went months without conversation, they always seemed to find a way to pick-up where they had left off. They both valued the rarity of their friendship.

Even though it was barely 6:30 in the morning, the city was restless as people began their day. The fruit stands began popping up on the corners of avenues and the breakfast carts tempted with bagels and pastries in their tiny windows. People cycled in and out of coffee shops fueling up for the day with espressos and breakfast sandwiches. However, it wasn't the busy streets that first caught the attention of the two friends, but a squat old man in a wooden sailboat doing his best to keep his boat square. They watched in admiration as the old man gently released the halyard to allow the beaten sail to tighten against the wind. In one sudden movement the old wooden mast let out a howling creak as the mast opened, the white sail filling with wind, and pulled the boat eastwardly to greet the rising sun.

Finally, Peter broke the silence and pointed at the old man in his boat, "Remember when we used to come down here in the morning before heading into the office? We'd drink our coffee and shared our dreams to own one of those. Except as I recall you wanted a 180' Schooner Yacht to sail the Mediterranean." Peter's short laugh echoed across the water.

One corner of Alex's lips tilted up in an attempted smirk as he stifled a sigh, "Yeah, and we vowed never to live in Jersey!"

Peter chuckled as the two of them gazed at the buildings on the other side of the river in the much abused state. "We sure had some lofty goals 20 years ago, I can't believe a love of boats and disdain for Jersey was all it took, huh?"

"I suppose," answered Alex, taking another sip of his coffee. Another bird called out overhead and he tilted his head back as far as it could go, just to follow its flight. He had never noticed how varied the color of their feathers were, or how the tips of their wings were so fine you could nearly see through them.

"Is something wrong?" Peter's concern cut through the moment. Alex's head snapped down as he met his friend's worried gaze.

"Well..." Alex paused to think of the right words to say. Swallowing the lump forming in his throat, he drew in a shaking breath. He decided just to answer the question in the same manner he did most things; short, quick and to the point. "Everything's the matter" Alex grumbled. "Everything."

Peter's eyes widened in shock. He wasn't quite sure how to respond to Alex's outburst.

Alex squared his shoulders and stood up straighter. He needed to pull himself together before the tears that lined his eyes had a chance to spill over. He sniffed and cleared his throat with a small cough. Blinking in the salty air a few more times he looked at the only man he could remotely count on as his best friend. This man helped him start Moss Global Solutions, and as those memories came flooding back, the decisions and consequences of the past 15 years hit him like a freight train.

"What do you mean everything?" Peter scoffed. It was clear now that Alex didn't call him the Chelsea Pier just to have coffee and visit. "It can't be that bad. I know our 3rd quarter earnings were behind expectations and we didn't land the automotive account, but...everything?" Peter ticked off facts on his fingers as he continued, "Alex, don't forget your company employs approximately 180 people, offers Internet solutions to over 4,000 companies worldwide, and even though we are not likely to hit projections this year, we will probably earn upwards to $10 million in profits! And to top it off, you get to fly around as a bachelor on a company jet or hang out on your yacht and sail off to God knows where...so seriously, what in the world could *you* be worried about?"

"Is that how you measure success? Money, boats, corporate jets and living it up alone as a bachelor? Peter, you are deeper than that. I once thought that to, but I never in a million years thought you would define success in the same way I do...or did." Alex corrected himself.

"Ok, come on, man. What's really going on here? You ask me to meet you at our old brainstorming spot that we haven't been to in ten years—at least—and I'm thinking you were finally going to announce a company Christmas Bonus or something. Now I feel like Clark Griswold who has to go back and tell his family we are not getting a pool this summer! We've known each other for far too long to beat around the bush, what in the hell is going on Alex?"

This time Alex let the sigh fully escape his lungs and his shoulders sagged under the release. "After I collapsed in Detroit, the doctors ran some tests and they found cancer in my colon. Well, it started there and now it has spread all over. They tell me there is not much I can do about it and I have six months...maybe less."

Silence met his proclamation and he couldn't bring himself to look at his friend's face. He trained his gaze on the flotsam swaying with the current, hoping he wouldn't have to break the tension.

"Oh my God, you're serious aren't you?"

With a forced chuckle Alex finally looked at his friend. "Even I wouldn't joke about this."

"No, no you wouldn't." Peter shook his head in disbelief. Now he was the one to look away, hoping Alex couldn't see the tear that was starting to form in his eye. He clenched and unclenched his jaw. "Does your ex and the girls know?"

"Hmph, no I haven't told anyone, other than the doc and my assistant Carly. She had to run errands for me last week while I was locked up in the hospital. Other than them, you're the first to know."

"I'm so sorry Alex," Peter insisted. "I heard about the collapse, but no one knew what really happened. I mean, you were out of town and all. I just heard through the grapevine it was exhaustion, but I knew better. I mean, you have more energy than a team full of high school cheerleaders!"

Alex laughed.

"Still," Peter chewed on his lower lip, glancing sideways at his friend as they both faced the water, "you should tell Samantha and the kids. They'd want to know."

Alex grimaced, "Samantha might break out the champagne after that nasty divorce we went through, and the kids are so wrapped up in their lives, I'd doubt they'd noticed if I was gone."

"Wow, Alex Moss, being self-deprecating, I never thought I'd see the day." Peter gave Alex a soft punch on the arm. "I'm sure she will be upset about it, and I know the kids will be. How are you holding up?"

"It was a shocker, that's for sure," Alex admitted. "But I'm starting to get my head around this and for the first time, things are becoming very clear to me."

Peter sighed, "I can't imagine the thought of dying. That must be extremely surreal."

"No Peter, it's not dying that I'm upset about. I'm upset that after almost 50-years, I never really lived." Alex rubbed his hands across his face. The emotions he had been shoving down for so long were finally coming to the surface. He didn't anticipate having to deal with them all at once.

Peter was silent in his confusion as Alex continued, "I mean, don't get me wrong; there are a lot of things I was able to do and places I was able to see that most people only read about. But it's the important things, some of which may have seem trivial at the time, that I missed out on that bother me the most. The girls dance recitals, cheerleading and school events. Hell, I bought the boat to take the kids out and they have only seen it a few times!"

"You mean the yacht?" Peter exclaimed.

"Yacht, boat, it's all the same. The point is because I believed success meant money, houses and things, I missed out on what was really important in life. And now it's too late."

"What do you mean, it's too late? You still have some time to make things right Alex."

"Yeah, I know. But not the time I would like to have. You know, I would trade anything to get that time with my kids back. I wouldn't miss an event and I would have been a better husband and friend," they both laughed softly in agreement. "Regardless, a lot of things are going to change Peter. I know I don't have long, but a lot needs to change."

"Obviously. What did you have in mind?"

"You never answered my question earlier, when I asked about how you measured success." Alex took the last sip of his coffee, even though it was nearly cold by now it still tasted good. He looked at the label on the cup with a small smile. It was simple, elegant, and modern, he liked that. Sometimes simple was best.

"Well, considering the fact that I work nearly 70 hours a week, but can barely make ends meet, I'm still working for my best friend— no offense, pal—I hardly see my kids and Emily's birthday is two weeks away and I haven't even thought of a gift yet. Despite all that, when I'm flying the world in a private jet and running a Fortune 500 company like you, then, yeah I'll feel pretty successful."

"But at what price? You already said you're overworked and don't get enough time with your family. Really? Just think about it for a moment. Is it all worth it? Even if you did have the money, and you aren't exactly broke now either, would you be happy? I mean, are you happy now?"

Peter resisted to answer right away as he gave it some thought. "I'm happy...for the most part. But, to be completely honest, Emily has been on my ass about spending more time at home and with the kids. And a few months back, in the heat of an argument she actually mentioned we should consider separating. I know she was just angry, but still…" His last words were barely audible.

"I'm so sorry Peter. Unfortunately, I can relate all too well."

"So, that is what you did, isn't it? All along I thought you were living the dream and life was perfect. I hate to admit, but I envied you - even was jealous from time-to-time seeing you with hot new girls and designer suits. I know things didn't work out with you and Samantha and I partially blame myself for introducing you to the wrong person, but you always said that sacrifice was part of owning your own business, right?"

Alex shook his head as he turned to face his friend. Placing his hands on Peter's shoulders he looked him in his eyes.

"She wasn't necessarily the wrong person, and yes, I did say that at the time but I was wrong. Now I know now it doesn't have to be that way. And that is what I wanted to talk to you about this morning."

"Oh great, here it comes!"

"What?"

"The catch, I know you need me to do something for you again, don't you? I'm not going to entertain one of your girlfriends again Alex, you know I'm married!" Peter laughed.

"No Peter, it's not that. But yes, I do need to ask a favor of you."

"I was just joking Alex, you know I would do anything for you." Peter confirmed.

"I know Peter, thank you. Well you know I have always wanted what's best for my kids. Even if I may not show it to them often, they mean the world to mean and I love them more than life itself."

"I know you do Alex," Peter patted his friend on the back. "And they know it too."

"I demanded they go to college and earn their way into the business. I've never made it easy for them and insisted they work hard like I did and they could one day take over this business. I realize I'm not telling you anything you didn't already know."

"Sure, sure, of course," Peter nodded and stuffed his hands in his pockets.

Alex continued, "When times got tough my only motivation was that I was doing this in some way for them. And now, just as expected, Amanda is doing exactly what I told her to do. She's working non-stop and barely has time for dating and I'm certain she is putting off marriage and children because of what I've done. "

"I know Alex," Peter shook his head. "I see her still at work sometimes when I leave at 8 or 9 o'clock at night." The thought, "she is just like you," hung unspoken between them, but felt all the same.

"She's only 27 for crying out loud and Allie is right behind her!" Alex tilted his head back with an exasperated groan.

"Yeah, that's a bit of a problem," remarked Peter, "So, what do you need me to do?"

"Well for starters, we have to find a way to change our business in a way that my children do not become a slave to it like you and I have. What I realize now that life is not about business, it's the other way around. Business should be about life! We have to have a very clear and concise definition of what success means in our own lives. My definition may be completely different than yours and that's okay. But if we want to develop a successful business that gives us more life instead of taking it away, we have to know what we are working for. Does that make sense?"

"Well yes, I think it does. So tell me, what's your new definition of success?"

"It's simple, and I know it may sound kinda cliché, but I can define it in one word - *happiness*. No, don't laugh. It sounds simple and obvious, but honestly I have to find a solution that results in my business making me and those around me happy. Otherwise, what's the point of being the boss?"

"So, what do we do now and how can we change this business to help make your girls happy?"

"I'm not entirely sure yet Peter," Alex shrugged, "but with your help, I'm certain we can find a way. When you go back to the office, I want you to see how things are running without me. I know I haven't been gone any longer than usual, however, now that they know I'm not coming back for a few months, pay attention to who takes on leadership roles. Let's see what changes are proposed and how smoothly things are running in general. That should give us plenty to discuss during our next visit. Don't you think? "

"That sounds like a tall order my friend, but I'm up for a challenge. If the end result is to be happy, I can't wait to see what's going on in that crazy mind of yours. So, I'm assuming you don't want employees to see you in the office. Shall we meet back at the park on Monday?"

"Nope, not the park and certainly no office. I've arranged for us to have dinner at Eleven Madison Park one week from Thursday."

"Seriously? How'd you manage to get a reservation for that place? There's usually a six month wait!" Peter proclaimed.

"Don't worry about it, I may be sick, but I still have connections!" Alex winked. "Is that time good for you? I would be honored if you could bring Emily along as well. My treat."

"Yeah, we'll be there. She's been bugging me about trying to get reservations since our anniversary last year. Now I'm very curious about what's up your sleeve."

"Curiosity is one of the many things I appreciate about you, Peter, but there are a few more things I would like to ask you to do before our dinner."

"Shoot," Peter cracked his knuckles, squaring himself for the task at hand. Sometimes saying "yes" to Alex Moss was like making a deal with the devil but, in Alex's case Peter felt it was always worth it.

Alex regarded his friend for a brief moment before pulling out a cream colored letter sized envelope from his pocket and revealed a sealed box that had been hidden under a bench. Peter took the envelope, turning it over in his hands. The thick envelope was sealed, but there was no inscription on it.

"That is a list of all of the many 'toys' and things that I've accumulated over the past 20-years. I would like to get everything on the list sold and the money deposited into a new charity that Carly setup for me at the bank. You and Carly are both signers on the account and the bankers name is listed there for you as well. My realtor in Colorado can help you sell the home in Breckenridge and a small aircraft broker is listed to sell the jet. I don't think I'll need the plane to get to heaven anyway, now will I?"

"What makes you so certain you are going to heaven?" Peter politely joked. This conversation had been too heavy for coffee and the sunrise that promised a stunning day. He was eager for any way to lighten the mood.

"Well, I'm not...but if there is a vote, I'm sure it will be a close call!" Their boisterous laughter frightened a Pomeranian out for a walk with its owner, and they were duly reprimanded by the feisty pup. "Besides," Alex continued after the dog owner continued down the path with an apology, "I'll have to work on that one myself."

Peter frowned, looking between the envelope and his friend. Alex was serious. "But Alex, don't you think you are jumping the gun a little? You can beat this thing! Are you just giving up?"

"No, no I'm not. I realize it may not make sense to you now, but it will soon. You just have to trust me. Look," Alex sighed in exasperation, "You're the only one I can trust with this. I really need your help. It's not like I'm selling everything. I'm keeping the apartment, boat and even Tony on board to drive me around the city. I won't be destitute, trust me."

"Ok, ok, fine." Peter sighed, turning the envelope over in his hands once more before stuffing it back into his pocket. "I'll take care of it. So, I'm afraid to ask, what's in the box?"

"Well, there's no reason to be afraid because I'm not going to tell you."

"Oh come on, really?"

"Peter, please. The contents in the box are very important to me and contain some of my most valuable possessions. You have to guard it with your life," Peter nodded in agreement and gazed at the box wondering what could be so precious to his friend and why the mystery. "When the time comes, I will let you know when you can open it. So, dinner?"

"Of course Alex. I look forward to it."

"Great, see you and Emily next Thursday night." With a pat on his friend's shoulder, Alex began crossing the large lawn behind him, heading back to Tony's drop off point. A few steps away he called over his shoulder, "And Peter, I love you, my friend."

Peter blinked in surprise, "Um ok. Sure, I love you too."

Discover Your Gift

If you could do <u>anything</u> with your life, what would you do?

Where would you live?

WHO would you spend your time with?

When you own your own business, knowing what drives you is an essential element in developing a business that satisfies your craving and instinctual quest for life's purpose.

Taking the time to become fully aware of the driving force behind your personal desire will change the way you run your business and your life.

Self-awareness is a focused process of understanding and acceptance of who we are. And who we are is made up of our environment, events that have happened in our life and the decisions we've made or failed to make along the way. As human beings who live in a complex and changing world, we often put our reactions on auto pilot by creating habits to deal with the mundane and boring issues that no longer hold our interest.

Without even noticing it, we drift through life making decisions subconsciously as we are driven by a relentless surge of learned impulses. While some of these impulses are positive and make our lives easier, others are affecting our business and personal life in a tragic way. For most of us, we live life this way without a realization or understanding behind it all.

Until, that is, we hit rock bottom and fall into the dark world of sadness and frustration.

To stop and pay attention to what is happening in your life is the first step in understanding why, at this point in your life, you are where you are today.

Without placing blame or playing the victim, you need to clear your mind of all distractions and take a hard and focused look to remember the events and decisions you've made to end up exactly where you are at this very moment. Sit in a quiet room. It could be in your home, a quiet place on the lake or in your neighborhood yoga studio. Take a deep breath. Close your eyes if it helps.

Relax. Become aware of your body. Clear your mind of all the clutter about the past and future. All that matters right now is today. This moment. Engage in the process of recreating who you want to become in a deliberate way. Guilt is often the reason for holding on to the pain as a way to punish ourselves for mistakes we have made. Resolve this guilt by admitting your mistakes and apologizing to the ones we hurt. Even if the one we hurt has passed, write a letter or have a spiritual conversation to express your feelings and sorrow.

Make peace with your past. Realize that continuing to bring pain on yourself may also hurts the ones around you now.

Let go. By letting go, you it doesn't mean you will lose your memories or recollection of your past. It simply means to accept your life for what it is and realize each and every day is a gift you have been given.

Cherish this gift. Don't take it for granted. Your new interpretation of the events of your past will shape your own reality and perception of your future. And it is your perception of your future that shapes your attitude and dictates your behavior to realize your true purpose in life.

Create your future !

For without purpose, life has no meaning. Living a life with meaning is the secret of happiness. You are not here by mistake. You are special. You have the power to shape your own destiny and improve the lives around you.

Stop and listen.

Find your true purpose in life and don't let anything or anyone stand in your way!

Happiness is all that matters !

PART 2
CREATING YOUR VISION

"If one advances confidently in the direction of his dreams, and endeavors to live a life which he has imagined, he will meet with success unexpected in common hours."

Henry David Thoreau

One week later at seven p.m. sharp, Peter and Emily arrived at Eleven Madison Park.

"Wow," Emily breathed as Peter opened the front door of the old Met Life building, "I've always wanted to see the inside of this place."

"I know," Peter grimaced, pressing his hand to the small of her back and guiding her in. She was trying to take in every detail of the space and he knew she'd likely bump into something or someone. He couldn't blame her though. He knew how much she loved interior design and art. It was her greatest passion and her biggest regret for not pursuing it professionally.

"I was hoping to take you here for our anniversary last year, but..."

"You've been busy," she nodded as they waited in the foyer for Alex to arrive.

"I've been busy, yes, but I was going to say that I couldn't get reservations."

"You mean you were too busy to make reservations and waited too long?"

Peter smirked hoping it would conceal the guilt tightening his eyes. Emily tilted her head up at him, smiling playfully, before kissing his cheek. She knew how hard her husband worked. Even though she didn't like his long hours, she admired his drive and respected his intentions. She just wondered if there was a better way.

"Well, I suppose you're right." Peter wrapped an arm around her waist, drawing her closer, and kissing the top of her head. His recent visit with Alex had already affected his awareness and appreciation of the moments he missed or took for granted. The top of Emily's head rested just beneath his nose and he loved burying his face in her auburn hair. The familiar smell of her favorite honey-lavender shampoo was always a comfort. Sweet sensible Emily. There had been so much he had wanted to give her, but in the process of building the business, he had taken his wife for granted. She wasn't the only one who stressed over his hours missed at home with the family. He wondered about what she must have gone through along the way. He wanted to somehow convey his gratitude and sorrow for her sacrifice. However, he couldn't find the words that would adequately express his love and admiration. Just as he started to speak, he heard an all too familiar voice approach from behind.

"Peter, Emily." Alex's greeted his friends with a warm embrace and Emily with a swift kiss on the cheek.

"Alex, how are you?" Emily returned his hug, "I'm so sorry to hear—"

"Don't be." Alex pulled back and rested both hands on her shoulders giving her a small smile as he looked into her eyes. "I'll be okay." Before the sadness in her face could pull him back into the depression he was sure he left at home, he gestured to the hostess stand. "Shall we?"

The hostess guided the small party across the terrazzo floors, and through the grand dining room. The tall open windows looked out over Madison Park and the city sparkled in the night. Once seated in the cozy black leather chairs, the trio enjoyed the opening of their dining experience. The waiter's assistant, white dress sleeves rolled a quarter of the way under his crisp black vest held the napkin wrapped water carafe carefully as he filled each glass without incident. No sooner had their water glasses been filled then their waiter glided forward, introducing himself as Joshua. In expert fashion he presented the menu for the night. It came in eleven courses, each more tempting than the last and with ingredients sourced from local farms. Joshua was so adept in his speech that his captive little audience were left with watering mouths after he was done. The Wine Steward then approached the table and suggested wines that were carefully chosen to match the chef's special selection of entries for the evening. Once Joshua confirmed that his customers needed nothing else he bustled away to the kitchen. The Wine Steward quickly returned with Alex's selection of the finest Californian wine available. It was Emily's favorite.

"May I propose a toast?" Alex asked.

"Of course," answered Peter.

"To a lovely couple who are part of a very small and select group that I call my friends. May you wipe out the bad memories and sorrows of your past, worry less about your future and live each and every day as if it's your last," Alex fought the knot forming in his throat and his breath caught before he continued. "Live with love in your hearts, a soft kiss good night and a life filled with no regrets. I love you both very, very much."

Peter's mouth pressed into a firm line as he was taken aback with the force of emotion Alex's toast brought him. "That's...that's very generous of you Alex, thank you."

"Yes, thank you, Alex," Emily whispered as she dashed a tear away from her cheek with the tips of her fingers. The three clinked glasses. Each glance given to one another spoke more than even Alex's words could have about the appreciation of friendship and life's little gifts.

"Well, how are things going on Hudson Street?" Alex asked Peter.

"You want the truth, or the socially correct answer?" Peter wiggled his eyebrows causing his table to erupt in laughter. There was no way he was going to enjoy this expensive dinner if they were all soggy with tears.

"Well Alex, there's good news and bad news. The bad news...," he paused gauging Alex's mood. He never knew how his friend and boss was going to take bad news about his company. Especially when it came to personnel. Alex's face was relaxed, so Peter soldiered on. "...is that its complete chaos over there. You were the glue that held everything together. Without your leadership, everyone is just fending for themselves. People are arguing about decisions that should be made, and they really do need you to answer some questions so they can move forward."

Alex nodded, pursing his lips as he processed the information, "So what's the good news?"

"I'm not sure if it's 'good' news," Peter braced himself to deliver the next piece of information. Things were getting personal. "But most of the employees seem to be happier. You know you did create havoc in the office from time-to-time with your new ideas and urgent demands."

Alex's lips quirked as he digested this newest revelation, "Yeah, I can be a bit of a tyrant. But that's why they love me, right?" His laugh came out short and nervous. He normally didn't care what people thought and had never operated his business from that standpoint. His current situation, however, changed his perspective.

"Yes, most do respect your dedication and commitment to hard work. But those are the ones who need your direction." Peter admitted softly. "They looked to you for answers. It's the clerical staff that seem the happiest. I'm not sure if many are working or just playing on Facebook!"

Alex groaned, "That damn program. Ever since Zuckerberg created that thing our production dropped."

"Actually Alex, while some do waste a lot of time, we could find a way to use the information to our advantage. At least that is what Brandy was telling me in marketing. She has really stepped up since you've been gone and created a new idea that might actually work."

"See? Where's your optimism, Peter?" Alex smiled. "That's good news!"

As they were talking about business, Alex watched Emily closely. Although Peter hadn't realize how he had taken his wife for granted until recently, it was obvious to Alex that the couple had grown apart. The demands of the business had taken its toll on their relationship and Alex silently prayed it was not too late for them to reconcile their marriage.

After experiencing a divorce Alex discovered that if he had known then what he knew now, his marriage would have been saved. Even after 10 years of being divorced he was still in love with her. It occurred to him years later that when you truly love someone, you will always love them. Alex let his eyes wander around the room, as his friends slowly lapsed into a quiet conversation about one of their children. He really wasn't taking in the sights of the restaurant around him, but it was a good excuse to let his mind escape to the past. He thought about his last argument with the woman he wished he had never let go. He didn't feel it then with the arguments, resentment, bitterness and anger that had entered into the struggling relationship, but the love was always there. He concluded that it was not the lack of love that led to his divorce like he had once thought. It was the lack of effort to court his wife and work on the romance which created the distance in their once loving relationship. Alex pressed his eyes shut as he saw a young couple at the bar leaning in for a tender kiss. He could never forget what it had felt like to kiss her, but the slamming of the door behind him as he walked away echoed in his mind.

Now, with his body ticking down its final hours, he had the perspective he wished he always had. He understood it was the little things like opening his wife's door, sending flowers without reason and expressing his love through words and actions that could have kept their marriage strong. Instead, he allowed his work to interfere with his marriage and he took full responsibility for his part in the failed relationship.

Alex opened his eyes once more and took a sip of the eight year pinot noir. Before memories of his wife and the trip they took to Napa Valley for her birthday could weigh on him further, he leaned forward earnestly, taking in the familiar pair before him. When he looked at the two communicating, it reminded him of how he and his wife were just before they were separated and later divorced. Exhausted and overworked, their dreams put on hold in order to pay the bills, taking care of the kids and manage the routine of life. His heart felt heavy with the memories. Even when Emily looked at Peter, you could see she was still smitten. He was just oblivious.

When Alex's marriage ended, he fell into a state of depression that took months to recover. He loved Peter and Emily and would do anything to keep the same from happening to them. They had a good marriage. It wasn't perfect, no marriage is. But they were kind and loving to one another and were incredible parents. It would be a tragedy to see the marriage fail and soon, Alex knew there would be nothing he could do about it. He knew he had to say something. Without another thought he blurted out a question which interrupted his friends' tête-à-tête.

"Peter, what makes you happy?"

Peter's eyes widened at the sudden question. He fingered the stem of his wine glass, looking into the dark liquid as if it held the answers. "Well, um." His brows furrowed.

"Family and community," Emily answered. She looked at her husband with a fond smile.

Alex smiled at the pair as he rested back in his chair and propped his elbow on the table, his fingers curling under his chin thoughtfully.

Peter sputtered, "Uh…well…yeah…sure, I guess that's one way of looking at it." He looked to his wife for reassurance, but she had turned to her Chardonnay with a blush. She seemed embarrassed for blurting out.

"Explain," prompted Alex.

"Well," Peter cleared his throat, before taking a generous swig of his wine. He looked around at the lively dining room that was abuzz with conversation. Laughter from the bar across the room spilled over, adding to the room's excitement. The energy of the room made him chuckle.

"I think what my beautiful wife means, is that I enjoy what family and community has to offer society. There are so many great things that can happen when people work together. Those sayings, 'Rome wasn't built in a day' and 'it takes a village to raise a child' wouldn't be possible without the community created by families."

"Fair enough," Alex nodded. "Let me ask you another question. Are you happy working for Moss Global?"

"Well," Peter hesitated, but a reassuring squeeze to his fingers from Emily encouraged him to go on. "No, not really."

"You mentioned, early last week, that you work long hours and never get enough time with your family. You seem to think that because I took that path and found success that you will too. But, if you're not happy, it seems pointless doesn't it?"

Peter gaped at his old friend. He wasn't quite sure where all of this was coming from. Alex had never been afraid of speaking his mind, but he had never asked such personal questions.

Before he could answer, the first course had arrived. As they picked up forks and dived in, Alex wouldn't let the question drop.

"Well?"

"Oh come on, Alex. What do you want me to say? That I haven't considered going into business for myself? I mean, it's logical, I'll give you that." He stabbed the tiny mound of food on his plate with a little bit too much intensity causing it to slide in its sauce, and ruining its artful plating. "But," he sighed, applying gentle pressure to his attempted first bite, "we all know the statistics of business ownership. Forty percent of business owners never make it past their first year and eighty percent never make it past their first five."

"So," asked Alex, "What are the other twenty percent doing right?"

"I honestly don't know," replied Peter with a hint of exasperation. "If I did, then I would feel comfortable taking the risk. I mean, hell, why work for you when I could probably do the same thing and open up my own business?"

"You make a great point, Peter, and honestly most people ask that same question. Logically, it makes sense, of course, but…"

"Starting a business is risky and takes a lot of money," piped up Emily. She would know. She had tried opening a small boutique jewelry and accessories store with a friend two years ago that made it only nine months. "Not to mention time." Her last words were a whisper and she quickly shoved her last bite of food in her mouth, preventing her from confessing more. Peter looked at her with tenderness. He knew how much that failure had cost her. It was more than money.

"The problem is—thank you," Alex nodded to the wait staff who had cleared their plates and presented the next course. Peter and Emily echoed him as the waiter left after a warm smile to each.

"The problem is," Alex continued, picking up a fresh fork, "that most people don't know how to run a business. Contrary to what most people believe, entrepreneurs like us don't fail because they think too big; they fail because they think too small and fail to invest the resources to make it work. And even worse, many of the ones who *do* make it, like us, are unhappy and would have been better off taking a corporate job with a nice retirement plan and corporate benefits. You see, Peter, what I've noticed after years of research is that just because you understand how to make the product, that doesn't mean you know how to run a business! It is not until you open an office, hire employees and start marketing your services that you realize you are in over their head and have nowhere to turn. You may know how to do the work itself, like a chef who opens a restaurant knows how to cook, but sometimes knowing how to do the work is the biggest problem of all. If the chef couldn't cook, he would have to find someone who did and it would force him to actually run a business!"

"True," agreed Peter, "but consider this, if the chef who opens a business hires the wrong staff and doesn't have great recipes, his business will fail."

"Yes, that is another perspective, but I think you're missing my point. What I mean to say is that it's not the food that makes a great business. Take this restaurant for example, the food is great, but that's not what makes it amazing. Why do you think there is a three or four week waiting list for people to get in?"

Emily jumped in, "it's the service."

The two men looked at her expectantly waiting for her to finish. She looked at them both with wide eyes, like a deer in the headlights. It's not that she was a timid person, normally, but she often felt a little intimidated by her husband and his corporate big wig boss. She worried that her own business failings would render her opinions pointless to them. But, they looked at her eagerly.

"Go on Emily," Alex encouraged.

Emily felt emboldened, "Every employee here from the busboy, to the waiter, chef and manager have greeted us and several used your name. I like when they personalize service like that. It makes you feel special."

"Precisely," Alex tapped his fork on his plate for emphasis. "Now, do you think the owner is in the kitchen cooking meals?"

"Uh, probably not." scoffed Peter.

"Right again. Matter of fact, I checked and the owner is in Italy for the entire month."

"Wow that must be nice."

Emily looked at Peter with longing. It had been years since they had been on a vacation and Italy sounded nice.

"You see," continued Alex, "the owner figured out that owning a successful business is not all about the product as you may think it does. Of course, the product is an important element in the process, but it's only one part. Most people enter business for themselves after becoming frustrated with their current situation and believing that owning their own business is the answer to their prayers. Corporate downsizing, limited financial opportunities and job instability make the idea of controlling your own future appealing."

"I kind of understand what you're saying, but I'm not sure I agree with your belief that the owner doesn't need to know everything about the business."

"How are we doing, here, folks?" The waiter had quietly approached and, waiting for a lull in their conversation, was now refilling their wine glasses. "Can I get you anything? The next course should be here shortly."

"Actually," replied Alex, "Can you do me a favor?"

"Certainly," Joshua smiled eagerly.

"You work in a three-star Michelin restaurant that has been around for quite some time now. Unlike most fine dining establishments that open too many accolades, this restaurant has gotten better, instead of plateauing. Why do you think that is?"

"Ah, that's easy," Joshua nodded, as he deftly corked the wine bottle and wiped its rim with a napkin from his pocket, "the owner of the restaurant had a vision."

"And what was that?" Alex encouraged.

"At a recent staff meeting the owner told us all that the reason we had earned the next star rating instead of losing steam to competitors was because he knew exactly what he wanted this restaurant to be in the end and then he envisioned what he wanted the people, who worked here to be like. He said he knew that if he held onto those visions that the restaurant would be a success."

"That's very interesting, thank you."

"You are very welcome, can I get anyone anything else?"

The trio exchanged glances before smiling at the waiter and shaking their heads.

"Great, then, I'll just go check on that next course. Ah! Here it is!"

The next set of plates were put before them and the familiar shuffling of dirty dishes and utensils being replaced was repeated.

"Now, do you understand? If it's about the food, would anyone really pay nearly $300 per person for these itty bitty dishes? As pretty as they are to look at?" Alex looked pointedly at Peter.

Peter paused, thinking things over as he finished his last bit. Finally, he nodded, "You do have a point. I think I'm beginning to see what you mean. It's about the experience. This is not an everyday meal, it's for special occasions and people are willing to pay more to relax, be waited on and taken care of at every moment. The owner had a vision, understood what his customer wanted and made that vision become a reality. He turned his dream and the fantasies of his customers into a real and profitable business."

"Good," remarked Alex, "you're getting to the same page I'm on. Now, that we see eye to eye on the true purpose and drive behind owning a business, we need to relate what we've discussed to Moss Global."

By now the last of the plates had been cleared after the last course. Despite the tiny dishes, everyone was feeling sated and weren't sure they could stomach another bite. Alex drained his glass of water, hoping the icy liquid would snatch him from the food coma his body was slowly slipping into. Peter's eyelids drooped slightly, and Emily stifled a yawn.

The next plate that was placed before each of them produced an audible gasp from Emily. The men were equally impressed.

"It's too pretty to eat!" Alex's fork hovered over the confection. He wasn't even sure what it was, but it looked quite complicated.

"But if you don't," Emily waved her fork at him in playful admonishment, "you'll hurt the chef's feelings. Eat your dessert, Alex."

Peter chuckled as Alex's cheeks turned slightly pink.

"Alright, mom," Alex teased as he pressed his utensil into the frothy treat.

"And thank you for this amazing dinner. This was truly a lovely evening." Amended Emily, retreating into her composed self.

"Yes, thank you, Alex," Peter agreed as he spun his dessert plate slowly around, trying to find the best entry point for his spoon.

"I wouldn't have it any other way, " Alex admitted, "And all business aside for a moment, I know we didn't talk much about 'my condition' and I really appreciate the focus on something other than my health...or lack of it. I wanted to tell you both something that is very important to me."

Peter looked at his friend in concern. There had already been a lot of bad news and he wasn't sure how much more he could take. "Alright, shoot."

"Listen, I know there is always a chance that a miracle could save me. But at this point, it is very doubtful and I'm okay with that. No, really, I am. I just think its funny how life works sometimes." Alex snorted, hoping to alleviate the tension slightly. He smiled ironically, "It took me dying to find out that there is a beginning and an end to this thing. It is forcing a change in my perspective so that I've had to stop and think about how I was spending my time every day. And you know what I learned?"

"You're spending too much time playing golf?" Peter asked, relieved that Alex wasn't afraid to use humor to break the tension. The next few months were going to be hard. Everyone sitting at the table was aware of it, but with the work that was apparent before them, they didn't have time for tears and pity parties.

"Is there really such a thing?" Alex mocked before smiling at his friend and continuing in a more serious tone, "I found out that while I may have made a ton of money, I lost the things that were really important. I also realized I have no one to blame but myself. We all have dreams but very few people follow them. My father always said that he hoped when his time were to come that God would give him a two-minute warning!"

They all chuckled. "He was always such a huge football fan. But I kind of feel like that's the opportunity I've been given. Not everyone gets their expiration date handed to them. I now have a little time to make things right. That's what I'm going to do with my time. You only have one life to live, and you need to do everything within your power to find out what makes you happy. But the question I have for the two of you is, what are you going to do with the time *you* have left?"

Peter and Emily looked each other as Alex's words sunk in. He was right and they knew it. A silent promise passed between them as they realized they needed to take a step back and evaluate where they were and where they wanted to go. Those conversations had always occurred when they were younger, but for some reason, they just stopped discussing it. They allowed life to get in the way. Peter laced his fingers with Emily's and bringing their intertwined hands to his lips, kissed the tips of her fingers. A small smile crept across Emily's face, lifting her cheeks as she gazed into her husband dark blue eyes. For the first time in as long as she can remember, she truly felt appreciated.

Personal Accountability   March 21

Like it or not, your future is in your control! The outcome of your life is a direct result of the decisions you make or fail to make.

Most people start their own business for themselves after becoming frustrated with their current situation and believing that stepping out on their own is the answer to their prayers. Corporate downsizing, limited financial opportunities and job instability make the idea of controlling your own future appealing, but before making such a decision, you should first make sure that owning your own business is right for you.

There are unquestionably many Americans who start a business, work extremely hard, sacrifice personal time and are rewarded significantly for their efforts while others are not so fortunate.

It is believed by many the ones who failed at business didn't fail because their dreams were too big, but rather their dreams were too small and, as a result, their approach was too conservative.

80% of small businesses fail before year 5!!

NOTE: What is it that the 20 percent know that the others don't?

Notes

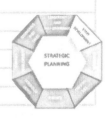

PART 3
THE FOUR LEVELS OF SMALL BUSINESS

"The foundation stones for a balanced success are honesty, character, integrity, faith, love and loyalty."

Zig Ziglar

"*Alex?*" *Carly peeked* around the corner of his home office. He had sat down a mere second ago, but she somehow knew he was there. It was uncanny how she was able to anticipate him sometimes. He had spent the past hour in his room, quietly meditating. He was wishing he had begun practicing the relaxing discipline years ago. He never felt more at peace and centered than after a span of time clearing his mind.

"What'd I miss, Carly?"

Carly entered, carrying her usual thick planner full of papers that included a calendar, contacts, and any paperwork he needed to take care of in person.

"Peter called. He sold the Breckenridge house, and all of the 'toys', as you put it. He's sending over the paperwork for you to fill out later this evening. There are also some insurance matters to take care of."

The word, 'insurance,' pricked at Alex. He hadn't seen Timothy Graham in years. He, Timothy and Peter had graduated college the same year and both Alex and Peter became some of Timothy's first clients when he started his own insurance company twenty years ago. The three had lost touch not long after that as each had been sucked into working for the "dream." Now, Alex's only contact with Tim had been through statements and policy renewals.

"You know what?" Alex grabbed a pen and began signing the papers Carly was continuously feeding him as if he was a ticket eating machine at a carnival. "Call Peter back and see if he can meet me at Timothy's insurance office this afternoon."

"Sure, just initial here, here, and here, and sign and date there." Her fingers moved across the page pointing at her highlighted lines he needed to sign.

Alex groaned, "Out of all the tech invented, there still isn't anything that makes signing your life away quicker?"

"At least neither blood nor wax is required," remarked Carly.

By four in the afternoon, Alex's Rolls pulled up to the front of Timothy's Astoria office. Alex and Peter approached the darkened glass door of the building, as Anthony pulled away to circle the block in hopes of commandeering a parking spot.

Peter tugged on the door handle, only to meet with resistance. He turned to Alex in concern, "I called before I left. His receptionist said they were open today."

"Hmmm, try knocking." Alex pulled out his phone while Peter knocked on the frame of the glass door, still tugging on the handle. Alex heard this phone ringing, attempting to connect. He warily eyed the "Open" sign in the window. On the fifth ring, a stressed voice finally answered.

"Hello…"

"Tim?"

"Yes, this is Tim. Who is this?"

"Hey Tim, it's Alex, I'm outside your door. Are you open?"

"Uh, yeah…hang on." A buzz sounded to let Alex and Peter in.

As they walked in, they could see that Timothy was over his head. Files were stacked two feet high on several desks, papers were scattered on the floor, old coffee cups still out on desks and the agent was on the phone with what appeared to be an angry customer. Timothy was sloppily dressed in blue jeans and a button down shirt that apparently hadn't been washed in a few weeks and his hair, what was left of it, was pointing in all directions.

"Yes, I know. Yes, of course, I'll get right on it as soon as we hang up and I'm sorry this slipped through the cracks. Alright, thank you and I'll let you know when we get that vehicle added to your policy. OK, goodbye." Timothy took a deep breath as he hung up the phone and greeted his old friends. "Hey guys, how are you? I'm sorry about that…crazy customers don't understand how difficult it is to keep up with all of this paperwork! So what brings you boys down my way? I feel like it's been decades since I've seen either of you." Timothy asked as he reached out to shake hands.

Alex spoke up, "Well, my assistant Carly called to make an appointment to come in and see you at 4:00 today. Didn't you get the message?"

"Uh, no, I don't think I did. Jessica is out…again! You know, you just can't get decent help these days. I'm glad you came by though, I was just about to leave and go get a beer. Would you like to join me?"

"Are you sure you can close your office this early…I mean, do you have anyone to answer your phones while you're gone? It's only four, you know?" Peter asked.

"Oh, hell. My customers know that I shut the office down early. I have a machine that will pick-up. Let's go have a beer!" Timothy insisted.

As Timothy grabbed a few items and locked up the office, the trio headed across the street to an Irish bar called Astoria Tavern.

"Mark! How are you my friend? Get me and my boys a Guinness please." Timothy ordered out to the bartender that apparently knew him very well.

Over the next few hours, the old friends got reacquainted as the discussed an array of topics including business, family, health, success and failure. After the third round of beers, Timothy opened up about how is business had taken control of his life, he was now divorced and felt like a complete failure at work and at home. At one point, he had even considered thinking about taking his own life. Looking back now, he realizes how foolish that would have been and how it would have hurt his family. He knew he couldn't go back in time, but was desperately seeking answers on how to get his life back in order.

Unfortunately, Timothy's story is not uncommon. Failing in business can have devastating long-term effects. Although his company offered a few training programs to teach sales skills and product knowledge, they really lacked in the area of teaching him business development skills. Like most business owners, he was on his own and never understood how to build his brand, understand who is customers were and why they would buy. He never learned to develop a professional sales systems, hire the right employees, set expectations, or even find ways to differentiate himself from the competition. Before leaving, Alex and Peter convinced Timothy that he desperately needed a business coach to help get him out of the hole he was in. Even though Timothy resisted and had no idea how he could afford the expense, he understood and agreed that if he didn't do something different, he would continue to slide downhill and the end result could be catastrophic.

"Wow, look at the time!" Peter slumped back in the booth after Timothy finished his story.

"Oh, really? It's only seven!" grumbled Timothy, "anyhow, I'm sorry you guys had to see me like this, but if you could give me until tomorrow, I'll have all of the paperwork you requested ready."

"Sure, sure," Alex got up and patted his friend on the back. "It really is good to see you Timothy. I wish we would have done this more often. Is there anyone we can call for you right now, or would you like us to take you home?"

"Home?" Tim snorted. "That is home now." Tim pointed in the direction of his office across the street. "Nah, I'm good. I think I'll have one more before I head over. Thanks for coming by. And Alex, I'm really sorry."

Alex paused for a minute and looked down as he was reminded again of his impending doom, "Thanks Tim. I really appreciate that."

"Alright," Peter sounded unconvinced that his friend they were leaving behind would be OK. "Call us if you need anything."

Tim waved them off before taking the last swallow of his beer.

"I really feel like we should have done more for him," Peter remarked.

Alex was texting Anthony to bring the car back around. "Trust me, right now he's at rock bottom digging down. When he's ready to climb back up we'll be there. Besides, I have a friend that owns a coaching firm who specializes in helping insurance agents break-out of situations like that. He developed a theory that believes there are four levels of small business and I plan to give him a call tomorrow. I'll tell you all about it in the car."

The grey car pulled up and Anthony quickly hopped out to open the doors. The two men slid into the back seat and as Anthony returned behind the wheel he looked into the rearview mirror at his boss.

"Where to, Mr. Moss?"

Alex sighed, and leaned his head back, seeing his friend like that and considering his own situation was weighing heavily on his heart. In fact, he felt as if his heart was in a vice. What if that had been him? It easily could have. Not that his situation was any better. He was just a different kind of failure.

His mouth suddenly dry and he practically chewed on the next words as they came out. "Take Peter wherever he needs to go, next."

"Honestly," Peter shook his head, "I cleared my evening to spend with you. Emily made other plans with the kids."

Alex pressed his eyes together again, hard. Another blow. "I'm sorry Peter. I hate that I'm wasting your evening like this."

"Don't be. Anthony, why don't you just drive us around a bit until we decide what we want to do?"

"Yes sir, Mr. Parker."

The two men sat in silence for the next ten minutes as the car slowly made its way through Astoria and other parts of Queens. The area was more suburban and small business in feel than Manhattan.

Big business were few and far in between, and Mom and Pop shops were abundant. Several streets were dedicated purely to different ethnic groups that had created their own "home away from home."

Alex finally broke the silence, "You know seeing Timothy like that and seeing all of these small business that we pass, it made me think of something."

"Yeah?"

Alex continued, "I told you about the insurance coach I know and his theory about small business."

Peter nodded in agreement.

"He uses Abraham Maslow and his hierarchy of needs to relate to business. Have you ever heard of it?"

"No, can't say that I have."

"Anyway," Alex sat up straighter in his seat, as he warmed up to the topic. Things were becoming clearer now. "Maslow was a psychiatrist who developed a theory that humans have lower and higher needs or desires and he used a pyramid to diagram their order. Without getting into too much detail, the basic concept is this. He concluded that if human's basic needs aren't met then their higher needs can't be achieved. But if all basic needs are met, like water, food, shelter, they can move on to the next level of needs which are security, love and family. And then, only if all needs are met, Maslow believed you could reach the highest level which he called 'Self-Actualization' and would be totally satisfied freeing you to focus your efforts on the needs of others."

"That sounds interesting. I think I remember studying that in college. But how does that relate to Timothy and his business?" Peter reflected.

"Well, I never really understood what my friend at the coaching agency really meant until now. I now realize how this could apply to people who start their own businesses, and the success of those businesses."

"Really? Go on."

"Ok," Alex licked his lips as he gathered his thoughts, "now go with me on this. Just like in Maslow's hierarchy, if the lower needs of a business are not satisfied from the onset, then the higher needs cannot successfully come into view and be met. My friend refers to the highest level as '*Small Business Actualization*' and believes when you achieve this level, the business actually runs on its own freeing the owner to do the things he or she had always wanted to do with their life."

"Ok, but what are the lower needs? I mean for a business, what would that look like?"

"Good question," Alex was thrilled Peter hadn't laughed the idea away and was getting into the topic. "Lower needs are the foundation of business development. Developing a strong foundation includes several steps that can create a blueprint for one's company. First," Alex began ticking items off on his fingers, the view out the window was now completely forgotten by both. "We need to define what it is the business is going to do for our life. Two, determine how our business will be structured to allow us to express our passion through our work. Three, we need to understand who our potential customer is and why they should buy from us. What is going to make us different from everyone else? Four, spend money on things that will make us money. This means that when cutting costs, we need to avoid cutting our advertising and lead services. Those entities create revenue for our company. And finally, number five. At the onset of starting any business, we should write out job descriptions for every position which will be filled even before our employees are hired."

"Oh, right," Peter nodded his head, "everyone always forget about putting those job descriptions together and just start hiring based on an impressive resume instead of what they actually need."

"Right," agreed Alex. "These descriptions will be templates that need to have compensation, benefits, and minimum expectations already decided upon. The problem is, most business owners, like Timothy, skip the first level and try to jump to Level II. When they do that, it makes it very difficult to go back and re-create their business and their business ends up running them instead of the other way around."

"Well, I think we know that's true!" Peter exclaimed. "Ok, so if the business owner manages to build this kind of foundation for their company, then what? Where do they go from there, how do they maintain this level of performance so they don't become a slave to their business?"

"Well, we definitely have a perfect example in ourselves and with Tim on what not to do. I know I'm not an alcoholic, and didn't have to file for bankruptcy, but his consequences could easily have been mine. Goodness knows we are all on the same path right now. I actually started to make a list of what someone who has achieved Small Business Actualization looks like."

"I like the reference to Maslow and Small Business Actualization. It's catchy."

"Yeah, I think so to. We've been making so many changes lately, that I've started writing down what I've been learning through this process. I don't know if anyone will ever see it, but maybe it could help someday. Wanna hear the list?"

"Of course!" Peter urged.

"Ok, here goes---," Alex pulled out a folded piece of paper that was actually a business envelope. He had written the list at the breakfast table just this morning. "They embrace the facts and realities of the marketplace rather than denying or avoiding them. They are spontaneous and quickly adapt to change. They are creative and see an opportunity in every market shift. They are interested in solving problems, and it is often the focus in their product development. And, their businesses run by systems which are fully internalized and inter-dependent."

"Hmmm," Peter rubbed his chin in thought as the car crossed into Manhattan. They were soon engulfed on both sides by towering buildings. "I like those. Could I add a few?"

"Let's hear it!"

Peter took a few more minutes to think. He even opened and closed his mouth a few times as he furrowed his brow. He wanted to get the words just right.

"Spit it out man!"

"Ok, ok! How about--- They appreciate life and run their businesses rather than letting their businesses run their lives."

"Good, good. Keep it coming." Alex pulled out a pen from his breast pocket and wrote Peter's suggestion down.

"They view things in an objective manner, and they take full responsibility for their own successes and failures throughout their career."

"See, you're getting the hang of this." Alex beamed at his best friend in pride.

"Yeah, I think I am."

"I just wish I could have thought of this concept further, and that Tim had known about this before he started that company twenty years ago," Alex remark with a sigh.

"Now all he has is regrets when the goal was happiness."

"Precisely, my friend." Alex's voice was sad as he tucked the paper away in his pocket.

Important !!

Hastings Hierarchy of Business Development

Every great business
has a solid foundation

- Small Business Actualization
- LEVEL 4 — Departmentalization
- LEVEL 3 — Systems Development
- LEVEL 2 — Foundation Development
- LEVEL 1

The Business Foundation Includes:

✓ Clear vision of the business model

✓ Business plan and org chart (Sales, Ops, Finance)
✓ Defined market strategy and prod. differentiation
✓ Defined Employee Agreements and Responsibilities
✓ Pay structure and incentive programs
✓ Documented Sales Scripts and Training Program
✓ Clear budget plan

Notes ✓

STRATEGIC PLANNING

PART 4
REINVENTING YOUR BRAND

"If you can't do great things, do small things in a great way."

Napoleon Hill

The past two days had threatened the return of winter with chilly temperatures, strong winds, and heavy rain. But today, spring had decided to assert herself once more, and for that Peter was thankful. Alex had canceled twice because of the weather, without saying why, but now that Peter had the day's itinerary he understood. Today was definitely a perfect day for a movie and the rowboats in Central Park.

Peter's two boys, Ethan and Ben had been begging him to take them to see the new Lego Movie since its release last week. They even turned down the chance to see it with friends because they wanted to see it with their father more. Neither of them could forget the lazy Sunday afternoons they used to spend building Legos with their dad. It had been a long time since they had had one of those Sundays. They would find themselves still in their pjs with pizza from the pizzeria on the corner stacked in boxes on the coffee table, and tiny cans of root beer. The root beer was their one soda indulgence of the week and within ten minutes of play, the living room was clearly hosting "boy time."

But, for the past year Peter had been so busy with work, Sunday time with dad had fallen by the wayside and his ten and twelve year old sometimes wondered if their dad even remembered they existed. So, when Peter broke the news that Uncle Alex was taking them to see the Lego Movie and then to the Boat House in Central Park, the two couldn't get their hoodies and sneakers on fast enough.

The tile hallway of their building rang with their excited young voices as they chattered non-stop during the elevator ride down and out into the lobby. They discussed their favorite characters, quoted lines from the trailer, and discussed what they thought the story was going to be about. They of course peppered their father with questions and it didn't take long before their enthusiasm sizzled in his veins as well. With a nodded greeting and a grin to their doorman, Louis, the three of them stepped out into the slightly cool air. Even though the theater was around the corner and one block away, Peter had had a hard time getting the boys to wait, and since Alex was meeting them there, they decided getting to the cinema a little early wouldn't hurt anything. Both boys were bouncing on the balls of their feet, impatiently waiting for the walk signal at the lights. Once at the theater, they were surprised to see Alex already waiting in the movie line in the lobby. He waved them over with a handful of tickets and quickly passed them out the minute the boys were near.

"Uncle Alex! Uncle Alex!" they chimed and before Peter and Alex had the chance to greet one another with a hearty hand shake the boys were off again, repeating their conversation from the building and reveling in their new audience.

"Hey Ben! Hey Ethan!" A boy with tight blond curls and big brown eyes greeted them warmly, he was a friend who lived in the building and provided an adequate diversion. Before long the three boys were huddled in tight group, talking animatedly.

"Whew!" Alex pantomimed wiping sweat off his brow. "I don't think I've ever seen them this excited! Fortunately Carly educated me on Fandango and I got the tickets early. They were sold out when I arrived."

"Yeah, well—," Peter glanced up and down the line, noticing other haggard parents surrounded by their enthusiastic broods. Peter cleared his throat before examining the tips of his shoes, still avoiding his friend's searching gaze.

"Well?" Alex knocked his boot against Peter's sneaker.

"Remember Boy's Day Sunday that the kids and I used to have?"

"Of course! You guys loved it. I remember how you seemed to be the only one looking fresh on Monday mornings. I swear it was because you spent the majority of Sunday in your pjs, eating pizza and playing on the floor with the kids."

"Right," Peter's gaze flickered guiltily over to his two boys. Ben was jumping up and down in excitement, his green hoodie falling off his shoulders and laces coming undone again. Ethan was running his fingers through his tawny brown hair as he explained something very serious to his friend. He soon looked like a porcupine. *Humph*, Peter thought, *just like me.*

He could feel his friend's impatience rolling off of him in tense waves as he awaited Peter's answer. Releasing a small sigh, Peter 'fessed up. "I've just been too busy, you know with the new acquisitions and the bigger accounts that I had to give up Sundays with the kids."

Alex tilted his head back with a small groan of frustration, "How long?"

Peter shrugged, stuffing his hands in the pocket of his jacket. "Ten months, maybe a year, I dunno."

"Looks like I couldn't have started this turn over at a better time. For both of us."

Peter looked at Alex, a strange expression tightening his mouth before he blurted out, "You would have been great with a son. I mean," Peter shook his head, back peddling his comment as a look of stricken grief flash across Alex's face before he blinked rapidly, looking away. "I know you love the girls, but you would have been really great with a boy, too."

Their conversation was put on hold as the line to get into the movie began moving. Once inside the theater all topics of business or the company were laid to rest and the focus was solely on the boys and their excitement over the movie.

As the lights dimmed and an announcement came on the screen about turning off all cell phones, Alex leaned over to whisper to Peter. "I never thought I'd see the day when there would be a movie about Legos!"

"I know!" replied Peter in hushed tones. "There are full on Lego stores now because they have more options than building cities. Just about every big movie franchise out there geared toward the male audience has Lego sets. They even have stuff for girls now, too!"

Alex looked at Peter with wide eyes. He was intensely curious about this new detail, but with previews starting he settled back with his big tub of extra buttered popcorn. It was a good thing he had wanted to talk to Peter about branding for the company next because it was obvious that Lego had taken branding to a whole new level.

After the movie, the fun continued, but the business talk did not. Peter attempted a few questions or thoughts, but Alex wanted to be sure the boys got all the attention they wanted. He could see how they were starved for their father's time and he didn't want to take away from that. They got ice cream on the way to the Boat House and then spent the next hour pretending to be pirates on the Central Park Lake. The ducks didn't take too kindly to being sieged upon.

With their sides hurting from laughter after being chased back to the docks by one very angry Mallard, the four conquerors stumbled out of the boats.

"Wow! I can't believe we've been bested by a duck!" Peter whipped tears of laughter running down his nose as he helped the boys out of the boat.

"He was pissed! Ha-ha!" Alex replied before making his way to the shack to retrieve their deposits. Once everything was settled the foursome strolled along the path, making their way out of the park and to the nearest subway line.

"Alex? Thank you for showing us a good time today. We really enjoyed it."

"Oh, well, it was my pleasure! Did you boys have a good time?" He placed a hand on each tousled head and rumpled their curls more.

"Yeeessss!" The boys chorused followed by "thank yous" and several sticky hugs and kisses to the cheek.

"Emily just texted me," Peter was staring at the small black screen in his palm with a pucker of worry tightening his brow. "Ah, ok." He smiled, shoving the phone back in his pocket. Placing each arm around one of his boys he drew them in for a hug. "Looks like your friend Owen is getting back early from his Grandma's and wants you guys to come over now. How does that sound?"

"Yayyyyyyy!" Their loud cheers and whoops scared off a tiny flock of birds that had been debating on the safety of retrieving some crumbs that lay near a bench.

"You mom is on her way to pick you up now. Let's hurry to the nearest entrance to meet her!"

As Peter and the boys set down the path, Alex swiftly followed behind. "Aren't you going to go with her? This may be a great opportunity to spend time together."

Peter looked back over his shoulder at Alex, "Nah, it's alright, she already made plans with her mother and sister. Besides, I know you're itching to tell me the next phase of the plan!"

Alex responded with a grin as they hurried along. Once the boys were tucked away into a car with their mom, and goodbyes followed by more thanks, the door closed and the car pulled away from the curb. It instantly disappeared in the cluttered Manhattan traffic.

Once the car had vanished Peter turned to say something to Alex, but he wasn't there. He turned around more, scanning the area for his friend when he heard his name being called. Finally, he spotted Alex on a bench a short distance away. Peter jogged lightly over before plopping down next to his friend.

"Are you ok, Alex? You look kinda pale."

Alex unscrewed the lid to a fresh bottle of water, and took a swig. He hadn't had it earlier, but a nearby snack cart was obviously the source.

"Yeah, I just need to catch my breath and get some H2O in me." Alex shook the already half-drunk water bottle for emphasis. "I'll be fine."

"So what'd you want to talk about? Are you going to finally fess up and tell me about the mystery lady you keep disappearing to see?"

Alex propped his ankle over his opposing knee and stretched his long arms across the back of the bench.

"No, there's no mystery lady. I wanted to talk to you about branding. Once again, it's technically something already 'figured' out if you will for our company, but I think we need to take a second look at it. Especially now that we've reevaluated who our customers are and what needs they have that we can meet."

Peter nodded, "I'm listening." The topic of Alex's mysterious trips that no one could account for was shoved to the side.

"A brand name is an immeasurable and invaluable resource, but it is also the most fragile in a way. Remember Tylenol back in the early 80s?"

"Oh yeah, there was a serial killer who had laced some bottles containing the capsules with cyanide and seven people in Chicago died. Of course the poisoning happened after the bottles were on the shelves and it wasn't Johnson and Johnson's fault. Still, they took a big hit. I think their market shares went down by what, 9 %?"

Alex nodded, he was slowly working the label off his water bottle. "It was 7%."

"Yeah, still, 7% was a huge loss and they ended up recalling all of their products on the market and stopped advertising."

"Exactly." Alex had now removed the label and was busy stuffing it into the mouth of the bottle. "Do you by chance remember how they regained the customer's trust after that fiasco?"

"Hmm," Peter ran his fingers through his hair, "I don't think I remember everything. They introduced some new tamper resistant features and offered a lot of discounts, if I recall."

"Pretty much," Alex said as he stretched his legs out before him. "They were actually the first to comply with the FDA's regulations on tamper resistance, they got well over two-thousand sales people to make presentations to the medical community, and they offered new pricing incentives to customers. Something that wasn't Johnson and Johnson's fault cost the company a lot of money, but I think it's paid off pretty well, don't you?"

Peter chuckled, "I'll say." The day had gotten warmer and even though Alex had zipped up his jacket further, Peter was quickly wiggling out of his.

"I look at a situation like that and at the Lego company and realize that these businesses know their customers and use branding to tailor their perceptions so that the customers will want their product instead of someone else's. That's something we need to work on in our company. We know who our customer is and what their needs are that we can meet. We now have the data from our market research to prove it."

"Right," Peter nodded, laying his jacket across his lap and enjoying the feel of the soft breeze lifting the sleeve edges of his t-shirt. "Although we aren't facing a crisis like Johnson and Johnson did with Tylenol. Thank goodness."

"True, but I guarantee you they had a crisis plan on file and because they stuck to their company mission statement of serving the safety of their public, the decision to take positive action was easy. I mean there are thousands of examples out there of companies having to re-brand themselves after a crisis or even after a couple of bad financial quarters. In the end, though it's all about understanding your market segment's needs, being aware of how fragile your brand name is, and being prepared to step up in the face of a crisis."

"Well, I guess it's a good thing all of those marketing reports that covered the demographics and the psychographics of our various

segments came back last week. We have plenty of info to go off of."
Peter sat up a little straighter as he spied a jazz band setting up a few
feet away. He knew that his conversation with Alex was about to be
interrupted by the music, but neither of them would mind. It was the
perfect day for jazz in the park.

"Yep," Alex grinned, for he too had spotted the group setting up.
"Since there are several different types of branding and we offer so
many different services, that's another aspect we'll have to sort
through."

"What do you mean?"

The trumpet player tapped out a few notes on his instrument as
the drummer finished setting up.

"Well, there is branding for your company and branding for a
product or service. We don't have a product, but we do have services
and the branding for those will need to be consistent with the
company's branding, but they also have to have their own feel to
them."

"Ah, I see," said Peter, "and I assume we'll need to cover
implementation and maintenance, too, right?"

"Of course. Everything our company does or puts out in the
public in any way shape or form needs to comply with our branding
strategy. A company's brand is in the eye of the customer. If our
customer believes our product or service is of good value, then quality
and value becomes our brand. On the other hand, if another customer
believes we are not fair in quality and price then, to that customer, our
brand now has a tarnished image. What I'm getting at here, is that it's
our customers perception of our product that becomes their own
reality of who we are. Perception, in everything you do, becomes your
own personal reality. The question we need to be asking is, 'how can

we, as a business owner, influence our client's perception of who we are?' If we can successfully figure that out, the only advertisement we will ever need is the referral from your satisfied customers. Our staff needs to be on the same page, too. As for the maintenance, branding is just another system of our business, so we will always have to reevaluate it. Society and culture evolves so we have to evolve with them."

Peter crossed his arms comfortably and settled back on the bench, ready for the show to begin. "Sounds like a good goal to work for. Although, I must stay, as long as jazz doesn't evolve too quickly, I'll be happy. I like it just the way it is."

"Now that's a perception I can get behind." Alex said with a happy sigh.

BRAND — Your brand is what your customers think or perceive you to be!

Who is your target market?

Why do they buy from you?

Why do they leave you?

What makes you different than your competition?

Review your sales presentation. Is it professional? Does it sell **you**, or just price?

 Consider writing a book or having someone do it for you to show how you are different. A book shows you are an expert in the field! It's cheaper and easier than you may think — Let a book be your business card!

Develop your personal story and sell yourself!

Review your customer contact points — your logo, website, social media appearance, email, letters and sales packets. Do you communicate a clear and consistent message?

Your success is dependent upon your ability to connect with your customers and develop a long-term relationship!

What is our brand?

PART 5
GETTING THE TEAM ONBOARD

"The greatest discovery of all time is that a person can change his future by merely changing his attitude."

William James

"**L***et us raise* a standard to which the wise and honest can repair. The event is in the hand of God." The quote by George Washington was inscribed on the arch dedicated to him in the park that bore his name. It was a fitting quote, thought Alex. He sat upon one of the many benches that lined the border of the lawn in Washington Square Park. There was a young man sitting sideways on the bench next to his with a guitar in his lap and sheets of music tucked under his crossed legs. The young man was picking his way through what sounded like flamenco music and every now and then he'd stop, grit his teeth, and with a determined look, would start all over. Sometimes he would growl at the pages before him in frustration if the notes got tricky, but he would always start over. To Alex's musically untrained ears, he thought the guy sounded pretty good, and was enjoying the lively atmosphere the tune was giving the scene before him. It was another glorious spring day, but apparently it was warmer than Alex felt. He only needed a very light jacket, but those around him were dressed in summer wear usually dedicated to the hottest of days. Sandals, tank tops, shorts, and flowing skirts; these were choices of the people who milled around the park. Many were eating their lunch, some were reading books or magazines, some listening to music, while others were talking and laughing with their friends. Children were clustered around the gurgling fountain in the middle of the park, and could be seen trying to climb in while exasperated parents held them back and tried the "toss a coin in" distraction. Many people were there with their cameras and others were there with their dogs. There was a jazz band playing in one corner of the park and a man knocking out a regular beat on some plastic buckets at the opposite end. Alex stretched his legs out before him with one arm slung over the top of the bench. He was halfway through his can of ginger ale that he often drank to ease his queasy stomach, but he was completely content. Normally the cacophony around him was not something he would have sat and enjoyed. The old Alex, if he ever spent time in a park at all, would have spent the entire time on his phone either emailing out missives to various people in the company or reaching out to clients to make and secure deals. Not once would he have looked up at the Greek revival architecture of The Village neighborhood surrounding the park, nor would he have noticed the people of the city enjoying one of their many parks. It was the people that gave this city so much energy and vitality, something Alex desperately needed and appreciated at this moment.

A small vibration in his jacket pocket told him he had just received some type of alert on his phone. His body, so relaxed and comfortable, nearly didn't want to obey his commands to move. If it wasn't for the fact that it could be Peter trying to get in touch with him, Alex would have gladly remained immobile. With a small sigh at having to break the magic of the moment, Alex pulled out the sleek device and checked it. Peter had sent a text to say he was leaving the subway station now and was walking to the park. Alex smiled, he sincerely hope Peter wasn't using the time to walk to stare at his phone the way both of them normally did. So much of the beauty of the city was missed when one looked down. Alex thought about telling Peter his thoughts on this, but decided against it. He needed to trust that the progress they had made in transforming the company was transforming Peter as well. He had already seen improvement. Peter moved as though he felt lighter, he joked more, spent less time at the office but was still just as productive, and Boy's Sunday Funday was back. All in all Peter was slowly regaining lost time, and even though Alex felt time slipping through his fingers, just seeing the change in Peter alone was making all of this worth it.

"Hey old man! Sleeping on the job are we?"

Alex jerked awake. When had he fallen asleep? He didn't even remember his eyes closing. He snickered, "For once I'm actually enjoying the park instead of working in it."

Peter grinned, "How many times have you come here to work? You only live a few blocks away."

"More times than I'd like to admit." Alex shook his head, "The pigeons and squirrels are properly terrified of me. I think I've had one too many heated phone conversations in this very park."

"Ha!" Peter's bark of a laugh barely made a dent in the rustle of noise around them, but it was good to see him so happy. "So," he continued, "what's the plan today?"

Alex raised his hand up to Peter, and Peter clasped it, helping his friend up. He didn't like seeing how frail Alex had become over the past month or how little energy he had, but his spirits were high and at this point Peter was taking whatever silver lining he could get.

"We," groaned Alex as he stood up, stretching stiff muscles that ached with lactic acid, "are going to The Topaz Hotel. It's not far from here, but we have a meeting with the owner in about," he checked his watch, "fifteen minutes."

"Sounds great, lead the way O Captain my Captain."

Alex smirked at the reference before shaking his head and heading toward Fifth Avenue.

"What's the meeting going to be about?"

Alex stuffed his hands in his pockets as he looked both ways down the street. They didn't have the light at the crosswalk, but no cars seemed to be in the area. A young couple holding hands next to him also paused a moment before heading out into the street.

"We've already covered Discovering our Passion, Creating our Vision, the Four Levels of Small Business and Reinventing our Brand, our next step is figuring out how to get the team on board. It's about taking an already quality staff, which we have, and getting them motivated to break out of their comfort zones and get excited for a completely new way of going about the business. When we started Moss Global we made lots of promises. One was to ourselves to one day take control over our futures and do something more with our lives. If we expect our employees to help us achieve that dream then we need to honor the commitment we made when hiring them. In order for them to trust us, we need to treat them like family."

"Well, you do like a challenge." Peter shortened his steps as he walked alongside his friend whose pace had slowed considerably in the past few weeks.

"I know you're thinking it's going to be harder with a company of our size, and you're right, but it'll be worth it. In our case we'll be getting our managers and project leaders on board first, and then they'll trickle the message down to their teams. However, the reason I want to go visit The Topaz is because the General Manager, James Sutton has already successfully accomplished what I'm proposing. His staff is a fraction in size compared to ours, but the method he used will be easily transferable."

"I can't wait to hear all about it, then."

The two men strolled down Fifth Avenue for a few blocks before taking a right on 11th. They didn't discuss business further, but instead focused on their shared favorite show, Boardwalk Empire. Before long they reached the boutique hotel that was nestled between a French restaurant and a row of brownstones. Peter pulled open one of the glass paned doors and the two men were immediately welcomed into the warm retro ambiance of the hotel. The metal ceiling was gold in color and cut into Art Deco like designs. The lobby consisted of overstuffed leather couches in warm browns and russet colors, the art on the wall ranged from modern to classics that meshed perfectly with the feel of the space. Even some of the lamps and other decorative details had a distinctly fifties feel about their design. The entire interior of the hotel with its burgundy reds and buttery yellows integrated the best design features of several decades that created a comforting yet elegant atmosphere.

After checking in at the hotel desk to let James know they had arrived, the two men sunk into one of the large couches in a corner of the lobby. A waitress from the hotel bar and cafe stopped by to see if they wanted anything to drink. After ordering a coffee, each, the men sat back and continued to take in the many details of the large room.

"This place is pretty nice," observed Peter.

"It is, and it runs like clockwork."

The two men sat in companionable silence watching the hotel staff go about their duties. Alex was right, not one person was idle. It was clear as each handled the duties of their position and interacted with the guests that they were all comfortable in their roles and were following the same game plan. It was easy to pick up on the team-like atmosphere, even when the staff members weren't working directly with one another.

After about five minutes the waitress returned with their coffees and an assortment of sugars and creams. After making sure her customers had everything they needed the waitress made her exit with a friendly smile and a reminder that she was available to provide them with anything else, should they have the need. No sooner had their waitress left, then James rounded the corner of an adjacent hallway.

"Alex!" he stuck out his hand in greeting, "no, no, don't get up! Stay where you are and relax!"

Alex returned to his seat, "It's good to see you, James. How are Carolyn and the kids?"

"They're doing well, thanks. Alice turned five yesterday. We had a princess and me tea party with six of her friends. I'm still shaking the glitter out of my hair!" James patted his perfectly coiffed black hair with a chuckle.

"Oh yes," laughed Alex, "it's been a while since I've had to suffer through one of those, but trust me, the trauma is fresh! Have you met my Director of Customer Relations Peter Walker before?"

"No, I haven't had the pleasure," James shook Peter's hand with a wide smile, "Nice to meet you Peter."

"Likewise," Peter returned James' handshake and smile with warmth.

"So," James hiked up the fabric of his navy slacks slightly as he sat in a modern leather chair next to the couch, "What can I help you gentlemen with?"

Alex ripped open two packets of sugar before dumping them into his coffee, "Remember how you told me about those Business Development meetings you have with your staff and how successful they've been?"

"I remember," James nodded, crossing his legs and settling back in his seat.

"Well, we are making some changes to my company at present and Peter is planning and facilitating the entire everything. I was hoping you could let him in on the process and how it worked for you."

"Most definitely. I guess I should start with why I decided to hold these meetings in the first place?"

Alex nodded, raising the mug to his mouth to blow on the steaming coffee. The rich aroma was just what he needed right now. He was looking forward to not saying a word, but letting this brilliant manager reveal his human resources secrets.

"Well, it all started about five years ago," James began. "We weren't doing bad as a business, per se, but we weren't doing well either. Things had gone a bit stagnant, but worse than that, morale was really low amongst the staff. I began to see some concerning trouble signs. Employees were routinely late to work, or called in a lot. Some were bending the rules and giving too much of a discount and other employee benefits to friends and family. There were others who were just doing the bare minimum at their jobs. Change was desperately needed. I realized that my staff did not fully understand what was expected of them. Growth should be a minimum expectation and there needed to be consequences for their performance." James steepled his fingers together and a crease formed between his eyes as the unpleasant memories resurfaced. It was clear how much he loved this hotel and the decline of his staff and the stagnation of his business bothered him. "I was working with a business coach at the time and he suggested the concept of Business Development meetings. The first step was for me to put an agenda together. I knew I wanted to open the meeting off on a positive note. I wanted to retell the company's story and remind my staff of our mission and purpose. I was hoping that my passion and conviction for this place would come through and touch their hearts." James touched his heart for emphasis. "I then wanted to discuss where our company had been, the current state of things, and where I saw us going in the future. The next section of my agenda for the meeting was going to be the meat of the goal I was hoping to achieve. I needed to motivate my employees into positivity and productivity. We are most effective as a team when we think outside of the box and know we can respectfully disagree without fear of embarrassment or rejection. Change can be good and bad. It is good because it can create a level of excitement needed to build energy and momentum in difficult times. But for some, change represents an interruption of the norm and more work. I needed everyone who was willing and able to help take our company into the future to see that the new systems I wanted to put into were going to benefit them the most. The first system I need to incorporate, believe it or not, was to actually to create a system for creating systems!" All three of the men laughed as James paused for a moment to take a sip of his water.

"Now that seems like a system within a system!" Alex joked and smiled at his friend for reassurance.

James continued. "Well, since we really didn't have any real structure or procedure guide, the first system we needed to incorporate was basically a way for my team to recommend the changes needed to make our business run smoother -- and who knows better than what to do than the employees who are the ones doing the work?"

"That's true." Peter chimed in and nodded his head in agreement.

"One of the most effective and cheapest motivators for performance that I discovered is the use of a simple production chart which shows the ranking of each employee. Posting this chart for all to see motivates the staff because they see how they rank against their peers. Next, not only did we create a procedure document for recommending changes, we also developed an incentive plan for employees who made the suggestions for improvement!" James exclaimed.

"I would guess that was a huge hit." Peter confirmed.

"Are you kidding me? Just the mention of a new opportunity to recognize innovation and creativity made them sit up and take notes! One of my employees recommended during the meeting we install an 'Idea Mailbox' in the employee break room to remind everyone of the bonus plan in place. I told her I thought it was an excellent idea." James' voice got louder as he became excited to remember the events that took place during his meeting. "Of course, she immediately looked at me and asked if it was eligible for the spot bonus!"

Alex laughed as he asked, "That is great and a wonderful way to introduce a new idea. So tell us, what was the second system you wanted to install?"

"Right…" James hesitated as he was thinking about where he was. "Oh yes, it was creating a mentorship type program for our employees."

Sensing a lull in the conversation the waitress appeared quietly and asked her customers if they needed anything else. Peter wanted more coffee, but James suggested they try a specialty drink created by the barista exclusively for the hotel.

"What's in it, out of curiosity?" asked Peter.

The waitress explained the complicated concoction and an intrigued Peter and Alex enthusiastically placed orders.

"That sounds really interesting," remarked Alex, after the waitress had left.

James smiled, "See, guys, this is why having a high performance work environment and a mentorship program is so valuable." He leaned forward for emphasis. "The baristo that created that drink has created five others that have become insanely popular. We were recently featured in New York Magazine, partially because of him. Ironically enough, he was one of my biggest problems five years ago in terms of employee behavior and morale. I was very close to firing him. But after looking a little more closely at the structure of the company and at myself as the leader I realized, there were a lot of other things that needed to change. When I put these two new systems on the agenda, I was really excited about the change they were going to motivate. I knew there was going to be opposition from some people. Not everyone handles change the same way. However, I knew that I had to meet the opposition and resistance with positivity and show

how these new systems were going to give my staff room to grow. Then more people would be on board. I needed to explain in this meeting, step-by-step how these systems were going to give them room to grow and be innovative, just like my baristo has been. I had to show them unconditional acceptance as human beings and let them know it was okay to make mistakes, but that I believed in their abilities and competence to learn from the mistakes and grow. I had high expectations of them and demanded excellence, but because I continuously focused on their positive attributes and characteristics in performance, it raised their self-esteem and confidence. They were excited about the challenge of my high expectations. Meeting with them on a regular individual basis as a mentor helped tremendously."

James paused as the waitress appeared with the drinks. He beamed with pride as the waitress went about her tasks, placing the new mugs on the coffee table before them, refreshing the sugar and cream containers, and taking away the dirty dishes. There was nothing special or skilled about the task, but the waitress moved with a fluid and sure grace. She didn't spill any of the very full mugs, was respectful of the customer's conversation and space, and was organized in her task.

"Excellent, thank you, Jen," James smiled at the young woman. Jen smiled back and dipped her head in an appreciative nod. After asking her customers if they required anything else, she glided away with her stack of dishes. "Jen's peaceful demeanor makes her a favorite at the café and restaurant," remarked James, loud enough for Jen to hear as she walked away.

"I can see why," Alex replied, "I can stay here all day I'm so comfortable."

"Your techniques for encouraging and growing your staff, are really intriguing," said Peter as he eyed, with an amused smile, the art deco design that was drawn in the froth of his drink. It matched the design in the lobby's wall paper perfectly. That baristo had talent. He took a sip of the drink, carefully, hoping to not disturb the design. "So, after you detail the new systems, then what do you do in the meeting?"

"Recognition is key!" answered James, "I try to recognize exceptional performance in front of the group as often as possible. A little pat on the back goes a long way when it comes to motivation and encouraging repeat behavior. Also, I ask the employee who came up with a previous suggestion stand up and update the group as to the progress of system implementation. Some of them get a bit nervous while others thrive with all the attention. It not only helps them develop professionally, it allows me to see who to look at to fill future leadership roles when needed." James, bent down and lowered his voice to make the next point. "But most of all, the benefit from having various employees present ideas is that it gets them all on board with the idea. See, if the boss is the only one pushing ideas down everyone's throat, it tends to create an *'us versus them'* mentality. If change is going to be accepted, we can't have a divided team."

"We have certainly seen that happen on more than one occasion." Peter admitted.

"And then finally, at the end of the meeting, I open the floor up to any questions and concerns they may have. I, of course, attempt to address some of the questions but try to allow the department heads to answer questions when possible. It's important that I develop my leaders and give them the opportunity to shine. When the questions have been addressed, I close the meeting with a motivating and powerful message which usually leads to a huge standing ovation and team members jumping up and down and high-fiving one another ready to get to work!" The group laughed out loud. "Well, it may not look like that exactly, but they do get a little pumped up." James smiled and laughed at his own humor.

"On average how often do you conduct these meetings?" asked Alex.

"Well, they can get redundant and boring if I do them too often. I mostly try to keep things snappy, since people have short attention spans. I have it before lunch where people are the sharpest and not in a post lunch food coma. And, if the information I need to impart is better received in written form, then I address it briefly before handing the text out. On average, I find that holding the meetings at least once a month is most effective. Since the hotel is open twenty-four-seven it isn't feasible to have everyone there at once, so I generally hold two. One for the morning and early afternoon shift and another for the evening and night shift. Of course, each department manager will hold smaller meetings with their teams on a more frequent basis."

"How do you prepare your staff for these meetings? I'm guessing you didn't just spring things on them out of the blue?" Asked Peter.

"No," James chuckled, licking his lips after a taking a sip of his latte. Despite being an owner of one of Manhattan's leading boutique hotels, he couldn't help but enjoy the froth of his drink the way a five year old would. Foam mustache and all. "What I generally do," he continued, "is I send out an agenda along with all the meeting information out to my staff one week in advance. I tell them where, when, and times as well as if there is anything they will need to bring with them. Another crucial matter I had to address was approaching certain members of the staff individually before the meeting."

Peter raised his eyebrows over his mug in curiosity at this statement as he took another delicate sip.

"Peter, just drink the thing already!" joked Alex. "It's going to go cold before you get a quarter of the way through it!"

"Yeah, but look." Peter pointed to his still intact foam design. "You don't see that every day!"

James chuckled, "You should see the one he does for the drink he calls the Monte Cristo."

"Challenge accepted! Now, explain why you have to meet with some people individually before the meeting. That sounded interesting."

"Right. Well, before the first Business Development meeting, I had to pull a few people aside in order to prepare them. The changes being proposed were going to affect these individuals the most, some in positive ways and some in not so positive ways."

"Really? Did some people worry that these changes were created to 'phase them out'?" Peter curled his fingers in air quotes.

James nodded, as he uncrossed his legs and rested one ankle on the opposing knee. "That was a concern for some people. The biggest issue was that many thought, 'I'm not good enough, so these changes are being made to get rid of me.' Others worried that everything they had done was wrong or not up to par. Some were hostile about the news and became defensive, others turned passive aggressive."

"Oh no," groaned Alex, setting down his mug with a light clatter on his saucer. "Passive aggressive is the worst!"

"Exactly," agreed James with a grimace. "Anyhow, once I was able to address those fears, and had the commitment of these staff members to support and implement these new systems I was confident to move forward with the meeting. Now, that the changes are over, if I pull anyone aside before-hand it's usually in order to ask them to give a presentation or to let them know they will be recognized or promoted during the meeting. It's a lot better than being surprised in front of a bunch of people. Since these meetings are mandatory, I don't want anyone to dread them."

"That's probably for the best," agreed Peter as he finally gave in and gulped down the rest of his tepid beverage.

"Thanks for sharing with us about this meeting, James, and these new systems," said Alex.

"Of course! This has been one of the best things I could have done for my employees and consequentially my business. My business is nothing without happy employees who in turn make my clients happy."

"Indeed," Peter nodded with enthusiasm, his eyes shining. "So, do you think I could try that Monte Cristo drink? I'm curious about that foam design now!"

With a wave of his hand and a smile, James caught the attention of the waitress, calling her over.

Approximately thirty minutes later, the two men emerged from the hotel, blinking in the bright sun like owls waking up at the wrong part of the day.

Both were buzzing with energy from their drinks but it was obvious that the long meeting had taken its toll on Alex as he stopped for a moment to catch his breath.

"Man, I feel like I can run a marathon right now." Peter bounced lightly on the balls of his feet.

"You look like you're gearing up for a sprint! I might not sleep for the next year."

"I know!" Peter said breathlessly, his movements becoming restless.

"Well, since you're ready to bounce off the walls and I need to stop for a moment, I would like to go over a few tasks that I believe we need to immediately create at Moss."

Peter stopped bouncing, waiting for his friend's next assignment. As hard as it was to do, he had finally finished selling the last of Alex's possessions. The house and plane had sold quickly. He looked at his friend closely as Alex rested his shoulder against a buildings wall.

"Even though we have satisfactory standard benefits for our employees, I feel as though we really need to step things up."

Peter nodded, "I'm listening."

"Since all of the profits of the business have been funneled back into the business we need to start looking to give back to our employees," continued Alex as they headed for the subway. Alex had been taking his car less and less lately in favor of enjoying the city, but he kept is driver, Tony, busy with plenty of tasks that were going to position him for a new role in the company within months.

"What's the plan, then?" Peter dodged a man walking his English bulldog before he got tangled in the leash.

"Sorry!" the man called out over the near collision.

"Sure, no problem!" remarked Peter in a frustrated tone. He was concerned the leash or dog could have tripped his ailing friend.

"I need you to work with the accounting department to develop a program that I've already laid out and had Carly deliver to Sheila. You remember her don't you?"

"Yeah, the accounting department's new manager." No one could forget the grandmother who started her career late in life, but was quickly rising through the ranks with her sharp wit, and clever ideas.

"You got it. She should have had time to review the preliminaries by now. What I'm hoping you two can develop is a program that will take 15% of the companies' profits and funnel them into a profit sharing program. Distribution will be determined by employees' tenure with the company and whatever the profits are that year. So, like most profit sharing programs, it motivates the employees because the better the company does financially the larger percentage they'll see at the end of the year."

"Ok, that—"

"But," Alex cut Peter off in his excitement, "I want to take this a step further. Most companies will require the employees to put that money directly into a retirement or investment fund. Let's give our employees the option of cashing out at the end of the fiscal year if they so choose. They may need the money for a down payment on a house or a family vacation. You never know."

"Oooh, yes. I like that idea," agreed Peter as they reached the steps of the subway. "But Alex," Peter paused as Alex turned to focus on what his friend was about to say. "Not all of the employees are excited about what we are doing and there is no bonus big enough to get them to change."

"Well Peter, if our employees are not willing to change after given the opportunity, than we need to change our employees. But give them a chance and opportunity first—we do owe them that. And Peter..."

"Yes" replied Peter.

"The reports I've seen already show sales are starting to increase and we are just getting started. To prepare for the growth, we are going to need new people. Let's make sure that HR is on-board with what we are trying to accomplish and the new hires bring a fresh perspective and positive energy to our group."

"I'll get that done Alex. You get home and try to get some rest."

Invest in others

You must have capable staff — don't try to do it alone!

Have regular staff meetings — even if you only have one employee, keep your team focused and engaged.

Recognize accomplishments — Employees will repeat behaviors that result in attention...good or bad. Look for success and recognize it instantly.

Always start meetings on a **positive note**. Spend a few minutes discussing how everyone is doing and take a few minutes to talk about non-work issues.

Acknowledge success and give praise when praise is warranted. Ask your employee to talk about how they came up with an idea or implemented a program that is improving the success of the office

When you have extremely important information to discuss, send out an agenda before the meeting to generate interest about the topics to be addressed.

Schedule meetings before lunch.

Start the meeting **on time**—every time.

Keep the participants on track and focused.

Have a **structured reporting** format for each employee to discuss the prior week's results and the priorities to accomplish in the current week.

Do not tell participants they are wrong or humiliate them in front of their peers.

Encourage creativity. Face it, you do not know all of the answers!

From time to time, **ask for feedback** when the meeting is over. Look for ways to make the next meeting even better.

Once a year, get everyone out of the office and arrange to have an **annual brainstorming session**. Open up with a state-of-the-business and report on results. Success, failures and opportunities. Share your vision and goals for the upcoming year. Have staff participate and report on their activities and plans for growth!

Encourage creativity

PART 6
RECRUITING THE RIGHT PEOPLE

"If you hire people just because they can do the work, they will work for a paycheck. But if you hire people who see your vision, share your passion and believe what you do makes a difference, they will go to battle for you."

Jeff Hastings

"*A*re you ok*, Mr. Walker? You look a little green."

Peter shifted in the chair for the hundredth time since he had sat down mere minutes ago. The plastic material of the chair made an undignified noise as he crossed his legs, his foot bobbing up and down with restlessness.

"Yeah, I'll be alright," he swallowed thickly, his eyes shifting between Carly and Alex. Truth be told, seeing his friend hooked up to the tubes and connected to a machine that was pumping chemicals through his body, made Peter feel a little queasy. He knew it couldn't compare to the nausea Alex felt on a nearly daily basis, but as he swallowed again, he tried concentrating on his friend's face as Carly left to get him a Ginger Ale and a bottle of water. He was really excited to tell him about his recent trip to Google. Alex had usually done all of the preparation for the meetings between the two and this time, Peter took the initiative to conduct a little of his own research.

Google was well known in the New York area for its company culture and the nearly eccentric nature of the work environment created to encourage their employees to be at their most productive. In fact, Peter recalled several instances when Moss Global lost creative and enthusiastic employees to this "on trend" company. Every system put into use at Google to serve this purpose is actually backed by data, as Peter found when he stopped by for a visit, and the results were easily quantifiable. One of the associates he had interviewed while there actually mentioned going into the office on her day off because she loved being there so much.

Peter enjoyed his visit and came back with several pages of notes about ideas and was bursting at the seams to tell Alex. He was especially keen on using scooters to get around the office and the idea of bringing one's dog to work.

"So where were you last week?" Peter asked Alex.

"Oh, I had some projects to work on and a few people to see." It was obvious that Alex was blowing off his friends' question. "So, tell me about Google. I can smell the burning of the rotating cogs in your brain from here, they're working so hard! Besides, it'll take your mind off things." He gestured to himself and the tiny room.

Carly returned with the drinks, giving Peter a choice of which one he wanted to start with. Peter went for the soda. After letting the carbonation fizzle down his throat, and the ginger settle his stomach he began, "Well, after meeting with James at The Topaz Hotel several weeks ago, I was really excited about getting the team on board with implementing our new plans. I was even more intrigued about how to get the employees excited and on-board with change. I can't remember if we discussed it or not, but I remembered that we had lost several high potential employees to Google over the past year and I wanted to see what the big attraction was for them. Alex, I couldn't believe what I found out. When it comes to putting their associates first, they certainly took the concept of employee appreciation to an entirely different level!"

"Yeah," Alex chuckled softly, "I've seen the building. I love how they've integrated the feel of the city into the interior design. Carly?"

His assistant paused as she was packing up a few things and it was obvious she was leaving.

"Are you feeling better now Mr. Moss?"

Alex had been dehydrated before Peter had walked in and Carly had helped the nurse give him medicine to ease the nausea. "I'm going down to the coffee shop to get some work done and let you two catch-up. Don't worry Peter," she grinned with a nod to Peter, "you're in good hands."

Alex glanced at Peter before looking at Carly once more, "The best, but I don't want you working too hard. Make sure you eat something down there."

Carly smirked, "You're fussing at me to eat? Now, that's funny."

Alex shook his head as she left. "I admire her ambition, but that girl is her own slave driver and she gets so wrapped up in work she forgets the basic necessities of life."

"Humph," snorted Peter. "Don't we all? Moss Global seems to attract the ambitious sort. But back to Google. They continued the room's view out of a window by painting it on the wall that was blocking it, they have a conference room that resembles a tiny New York apartment, and there are subway grates and fire hydrants in one hallway. I can't believe how much they've been able maximize the space there! It certainly doesn't fit the typical corporate look, that's for sure."

"Hey--," Alex shifted in his reclining chair so he could sit up further. Peter picked up the pillow that fell when he moved, "--did you check out the library?"

"That? Oh yeah, I bet that room is your favorite!" Peter stuffed the pillow behind his friend's head.

"Victorian like pictures of Star Wars characters and secret reading nooks hidden behind movable book shelves? Uh yeah!" Alex grinned, pulling the blanket on his lap up closer. "I love their virtual library too, so innovative!"

"Well, they're a tech company. It'd be weird of them not to be innovative in that field. Hey are you cold? Want me to get another blanket?"

"Sure, Peter, that'd be great."

Peter left and returned after a few minutes with a warm blanket that he spread over his friend's reclining figure. The machine was still silently spinning away next to him, its display flashing numbers that looked ominous to Peter. He knew it was just because he didn't understand what anything meant, but still he didn't like it.

Alex noticed Peter scowling at the machine, "Oh stop, you're like an old lady fussing away over there."

Peter rolled his eyes at his friend before plopping back down in his chair. He grabbed his water bottle and took another swig before pouring more water from the pitcher on the side table into Alex's empty glass.

"As I was saying," Peter drawled, "When I got to Google, I met with Amy, an assistant to the Regional Facilities Manager and she gave me a tour of the building and introduced me to a few of the associates who worked there."

"Excellent! So, tell me what you thought of the work culture there. They really seem to value the creativity and innovation of their people."

Peter nodded, "And their health. They offer free meals and, I love this, they hide the "unhealthy" options like soda and candy behind opaque jars and cabinet doors and put the healthy stuff up front. They found through a study that people will gravitate toward the healthy stuff if they see it first. Clever, huh?"

"Now, that's a great idea! I'm sure if I would have taken better care of myself, I wouldn't be hooked up to all of these machines!"

"Uh, I'm sure you are right." Peter nodded and paused as an unsettling reminder of his surroundings was forced upon him. Trying to change the subject, he continued, "They also subsidize gym memberships, and allow the engineers to create their own desks, so some of them have treadmills or create standing desks."

"Why don't they have a gym facility there? I heard one of their California offices has a really nice state of the art one."

Peter shrugged, "Apparently, the employees here preferred to join a gym. One manager I spoke with said that the methods they employ to keep their engineers happy, while some might consider financially frivolous is very much cost effective. He said they work better with more space and that it really doesn't cost much to keep them happy."

"See, I like that attitude," said Alex, with a satisfied sigh. "Google really seems to understand the needs of their employees and it's obvious they strive to make the environment a high performance one by thinking outside the typical corporate structure."

"They really do," agreed Peter. "I spoke with one engineer who used to work at their Silicon Valley office in California and he said that each location is like its own city. They have their own benefits, quirks, and charms. However, each office really integrates what's important to the work culture in that area."

"That explains a lot, then. Well, they have certainly done a lot to retain fantastic employees, but I wonder how they recruited those employees. Did you speak to anyone about that?"

Peter took another sip of his water, but jumped when Alex's machine began beeping. He spilled half his water bottle down his front before he coughed and sputtered, "What was that?"

"Oh that's nothing!" Alex was laughing so hard he could barely get the words out, tears were streaming down his cheeks as he held his side. "That happens all the time when the medicine changes."

"Shit! That scared me half to death!" Peter was breathing heavily, "I thought you were going into cardiac arrest or something!"

"Oh please," Alex wiped at his face, still laughing, "That machine doesn't monitor that, and it's not like in the movies you know."

"Yeah, yeah ok."

"It's a lot scarier in real life," Alex deadpanned with a suddenly straight face.

"Really, has that happened to you before?"

"Nah, I'm just messing with you. I have no idea!" Alex set off on another giggle attack that turned into loud bellows once Peter's soda can pinged off the side of his head.

A nurse's head popped into the room with a concern look on her face. "Is everything ok in here?"

"Yeah, yeah Elyse," Alex wheezed in between laughter while Peter fumed. "Everything's fine."

"Ok," Elyse tried to hold in her own laughter in order to keep her tone firm. "Well, keep it down please."

"Yes ma'am." Alex saluted as Elyse nodded and left, clicking the door shut softly behind her.

"See?" Alex said. "You're going to get me in trouble with the teacher!"

"Ha, you were always the teacher's pet from what I can recall."

"Maybe," Alex replied with a smile. "So, tell me about their recruiting process. I bet they have some pretty innovative techniques. Even though we have a pretty decent staff, I'm sure that's another area of improvement we can make toward the future. Part of creating the high performance work environment we want is going to be hiring the people who can successfully implement it."

Peter leaned forward in his chair, placing his elbows on his knees as he looked at Alex with excitement. "Google is all about innovation, and as such they have five sets of criteria that they list in order of priority. What astounds me is that the priority given to the topics is not what I would have guessed at all, and what I think most companies reverse."

Alex chuckled. Peter looked like a kid holding a limited edition, mint comic book. "You look pretty excited about it. Tell me!"

"Get this"—Peter paused for dramatic effect like he was about to announce who was getting kicked off the island. "They value one's ability to learn quickly and to adapt to those discoveries above expertise. In fact they value three other characteristics over credentials. Someone's college degree or experience is at the bottom of their list!"

"Really? That is interesting. You're right, most companies would rather pick a candidate that has a certain type of degree, or a high GPA or even a certain amount of experience. However, it's really not surprising that Google would shake things up in this way."

"Why do you say that?" Peter leaned back in his chair again, flipping the tiny top of the water bottle he just opened in the air as he listened. He always listened better when he moved.

"Google has a firm grasp of their brand and they hire to fit that brand. As a tech company they are all about innovation and evolving. Their industry is a fast moving one, so people who can problem solve quickly, and learn and adapt quickly are going to be their best employees. Otherwise the majority of their "expertise" will be outdated before they hit six months of experience with the new skill."

Peter nodded, "Well, the recruiter that I spoke with said something similar in that regard. When they look at potential candidates and during the interview process, they look for curiosity. They also look for a good leader who exhibits humility, and can take ownership for what they've done, both good and bad."

"Those are very good questions," Alex agreed. "Was there anything else special about their interview process?"

"They were very organized with the entire process. You could tell they had a system in place and everyone was on the same page. They had a set of general questions to ask for the interview that pertained to the company, while the remaining questions were customized for the position."

"I see," said Alex. His gaze slid to the machine. The timer read ten minutes, and he squirmed in his seat slightly. The last few minutes were always the worse. He hated sitting still so long. He always had to be doing something, but this entire experience with the cancer had forced him to slow down.

Peter noticed his friend's agitation, and knew that Alex needed more than conversation to keep his mind off things.

"You know what? There are some great videos about all of this on the Google website. They are very open about the process. Would you like to see them?"

"That'd be great," Alex heaved a sigh of relief.

Peter pulled out his iPad from his leather messenger bag he often carried around.

"In the videos you can see the tour they often give interviewees before they sit down. I think the sight of potential co-workers zipping around on scooters and the ladder that connects the floors as an alternative to the elevator puts a lot of people at ease. Plus, it gives the interviewer a chance to observe the candidate in a more natural and relaxed atmosphere."

"Yeah, you can't be stressed seeing that kind of fun!" Alex leaned forward a bit so he could see the iPad better. This time he caught the pillow behind him as it began to tumble. Stuffing it behind his back, he focused on the bright screen before him as Peter clicked on apps.

"Exactly. They have a great way of keeping the interviewee at ease the entire time. They let them do the majority of the talking, and most importantly, they don't try to 'sell' the job."

"I know a lot of companies try to do that when they find a desirable candidate, but I can see why Google doesn't feel the need to. Besides, the right person will accept the job anyhow."

Peter had the video pulled up now and was waiting to click on it, as they finished their conversation. "I agree. No one should have to sell working at the company, or the position. Even when it comes to closing the interview, evaluating the data, and making the offer. Google is very organized about it and courteous to everyone's feelings."

"How so?"

"Well, they allow the interviewee the chance to ask questions at the end, but know that often questions come later. So, they don't make them feel the pressure of answering right away. They follow up with thank-you's, and if there is a rejection they let those candidates know. When it comes to making an offer, they already know where they stand and what they can be flexible on. They are prepared for everything!"

"Sounds like it!" Alex smiled as he realized his friend was excited again about his career and enthusiastic about taking on a leadership role in the organization.

"But I do have to tell you something Alex."

Alex expected the worst as Peter looked down at his shoes and seemed to be preparing to lay a bomb shell. "It's Amanda."

"What about Amanda?"

"I had sent her an email invite about making the trip over to Google with me and she just responded that she had meetings all day that she couldn't reschedule. If that were all, I wouldn't be concerned, but this is the third or fourth time she's blown me off. I know she is your daughter and all, but I'm not sure what to do."

"She'll be alright Peter. I know she has been working on some projects and has a lot going on right now. Just give her some time, OK?"

"Of course I will. I just thought you should know."

———————

After Peter left he stopped by the coffee shop at Alex's request to check up on Carly. He knew Alex would be happy to know that his assistant was busy typing away on her laptop, but she was also surrounded by several empty dishes.

"Hey, how's it going?"

"It's going well, Mr. Walker, thank you." Carly finished her sentence as she spoke and Peter could see her struggle to drag her eyes away from the screen to look him in the eye. She closed the lid of the laptop as if to deny its pull on her.

"Alex says you've been working overtime a lot, lately."

"Yes, well," Carly looked slightly guilty, "he doesn't like me working so much, but I don't like him leaving us, so," she clenched her jaw, clearly trying to reign in her emotion. "We don't always get what we want, you know?"

Peter was slightly taken aback at her brittle tone, and he wondered at his own mortality. Indomitable Alex, as hard and difficult of a boss as he could be, he still made a heavy impact on people. Peter wondered what kind of impact could be made if Alex had always acted in this way. If he was living a life of happiness and no regrets, what kind of positive impact could he have on those whose lives he touched? Peter wondered at the ripples he caused around him. Seeing the situation from someone else's perspective was surreal in an eye opening way.

"So, tell me," Peter sat across from Carly. "Why do you think he does it?" He pointed upstairs in the general direction of Alex's room. "If the doctors say it's incurable, why go through the pain?"

"Oh, well," Carly laced her fingers, pressing her palms together over the closed laptop and leaned forward as if she were trading national secrets. "I really don't know...but I often wonder if it's partially my fault. I begged him to at least try and fight this. There are always accounts of people getting better despite the initial diagnosis. You don't think he's in pain, do you?"

"Oh," Peter suddenly realized he'd said too much. "Maybe from time-to-time...but mostly he's fine." Peter waved the idea away. "But I'll tell you this, he loves you and is lucky to have you as his assistant...and his friend." He patted Carly on the back and got up to leave.

"Thank you Mr. Walker," Carly smiled, tucking a strand of her dark hair behind her ear as if she wasn't sure how to accept the compliment fully.

The self-conscious gesture saddened Peter as he realized that she, probably like many of the company's employees, didn't get enough appreciation. He resolved to fix that as he noticed that Alex already was.

Appreciate employees from the onset by creating a welcoming family-like atmosphere.

Hire employees based on the **needs** of your company. Find people that fit your brand. Looking at their "school" or "experience" may not be enough. Look for what makes them a great employee. Think outside of the box when recruiting.

Questions to ask to find those **"right"** people
-What does my company do? (It's product/service)
-Who are my clients?
-What appeals to them about my company?
-What kind of employees will attract them?
-What experience are they looking for?

Create job descriptions to use as templates, but every position should be specific. If I know exactly what I want for this position, it's goals, its potential future, and its requirements, I can always be on the lookout for the right people to fill the position.

Notes

Source your potential employees in the same way you source your market. Ask similar questions.

- who are they?

- what are they looking for in a career?

- where are they now? Graduating, changing careers? Retiring from first job?

- what is it about my company that would make them want to work for us?

- how will they appeal to my clients?

- **teach sales first!** Make employees earn your valuable training time. **Everyone** in the office needs to sell in some way. Develop an easy sales system and train new employees how to improve client retention, cross-sell and/or bring in new clients.

Higher creative thinkers

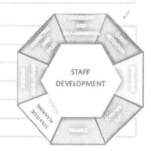

PART 7
HIGH PERFORMANCE WORK ENVIRONMENT

"Treat employees like they make a difference and they will."

Jim Goodnight
CEO, SAS

Alex wondered if he twisted his head any further into the awkward angle, if it would suddenly snap off. That was the problem with modern art, he sighed to himself. It made unnecessary demands on your presence, just to delight the follies of the artist who constructed it. Alex chuckled, his head still bent at an odd angle as he leaned to the right and looked up.

"Is this a new form of yoga you are practicing Mr. Moss?" A soft voice with a light British lilt caused Alex to stand up too quickly and whirl around to face the petite woman behind him.

The room spun, as he whispered, "Sam!" The next moment, Alex felt strong slender fingers grip his elbows to steady him.

"Mr. Moss! Are you alright? Here why don't you sit?"

He wasn't sure how he made it to the odd shaped chair in the corner of the room, but it was surprisingly comfortable. A small bottle of orange juice was thrust into his hands.

"Drink." His hands voluntarily raised the open bottle to his lips at the brusque command.

After a few sips, the fog in his brain cleared, but a strange chill ran down his spine. He recognized it from the last time he passed out. He rested his elbows on his knees, dipping his head between his legs. Gulping down large breaths, he was thankful that the spacious art gallery near the Highline was deserted. It was before opening hours and he was thankful that Samantha Martin had agreed to meet him so early.

At 42, the woman was a Phenom in the art industry. She was in charge of curating and running several galleries in the area and had a knack for not only hiring the most talented and knowledgeable in the industry, but also predicting the next prolific artist. Her taste was impeccable. If she liked it, it sold. Her employees loved her, even those who had worked in the industry longer than she had been alive. She was adored by everyone, and many said it was her knack for problem solving as well as her generous and compassionate nature. A recent article in New York Magazine had detailed accounts of her employee interaction and many mentioned that it was because she was concerned about them on a personal level that they knew she genuinely cared with their best interests at heart.

"Are you going to be sick?"

Alex peered up at the worried blue eyes hovering above him. It took him a moment, but after plying his dry tongue off the roof of his mouth he took another sip of juice as he straightened up further.

"No, I'm fine." He hoped his light hearted laugh would dispel the worried tent Samantha's blonde eyebrows were currently making.

He shook his head slightly, still trying to gather his wits about him. "I think I just stood back up too fast. You startled me. What are you, some kind of ninja?" He grinned at her.

Samantha straightened back up, although since she was so short in comparison to him, the movement was slight. Her eyes narrowed in suspicion, still not convinced.

"I think you should remain seated awhile, just the same. What were you doing in that ridiculous pose to begin with?"

"Sorry," Alex grimaced. "I thought maybe if I looked at it from a different angle, I would understand what the artist was attempting to convey. I mean he called the piece, "Perspective" after all." Alex shrugged, taking another sip of juice. "I don't know, I guess I thought that was the point. Look at it from many different perspectives. Right?"

Finally, a small smile akin to a smirk, tugged at the corners of Samantha's lips. "I suppose that's one way of looking at it."

"Pun intended?"

Her smile broadened. "Always. Honestly, though, the only reason I chose that painting was not for the artist's technical skill. A monkey with a paint brush could have recreated the same mess he did, but his choice and mixture of colors was very deliberate."

Alex nodded to the painting in question, "You don't think a monkey could have chosen those colors?"

Samantha's laughter echoed in the empty gallery. The receptionist at the front desk glanced up at the sound, a smile lifting her cheeks before she returned to her task.

"A monkey may have chosen the same colors, but I don't think he could have assembled them so purposefully. Despite the vagueness of the painting, the color palette resides in a very uniform structure. That's what makes this work brilliant."

"Sounds like it's a delightful oxymoron, then."

"I've never thought of it that way, but yes." Samantha scanned over the room, "Where's Peter?"

"Home. One of the boys is sick with the stomach flu, and usually his wife stays home with them, but she was just asked by very famous celebrity, whom I'm not allowed to name, to help design the interior of her new penthouse."

"Are you serious?" Samantha's eyes glittered with excitement over the revelation, but she made no attempt to pry. Like any shrewd business woman, news of opportunity always drew intrigue. As someone who often catered celebrity clients, however, she knew how to respect confidentiality.

"Deadly serious," Alex nodded. His heart fell slightly as the words left his lips. Over the past few weeks he began to notice the irony in throw away phrases that reference life, death or disease in any way. "This is the opportunity she's been waiting for and I believe Peter realizes if his career gets in the way this time, it may be his last!" They both chuckled.

"Well," Samantha crossed her arms comfortably. "While I'm glad Peter is taking the initiative, I'm shocked he was able to drag himself away from his work long enough. Or is he going to work from home?" Her eyebrow lifted in challenge. Alex knew she was never fond of their non-stop work style.

"No. He could, but if he did, we both know Ethan wouldn't get much attention. I made Peter promise that he would only touch work if Ethan was sleeping. I think they have just started their Star Wars marathon right now, though, so we'll see."

"Good," Samantha nodded, "I'm glad to see you are both coming to your senses. Now, what is it that was so important that I canceled an appointment to see you today?"

Alex felt bad that he was still sitting while Samantha stood in her impossibly high heels. He wondered again how she had managed to sneak up on him in those things. He slowly stood, thankful that the room decided to remain motionless. Samantha held out a hand in caution, but before she could drop it again, Alex snatched it up and bowed over it.

"Milady."

Samantha laughed, lightly slapping him on the shoulder, "You're impossible."

"You don't have any rings to kiss. That was no fun!" Alex made his way back over to the painting. Now that he understood what he was looking at, he felt he could enjoy it more. Samantha followed closely behind, while still giving him the quiet and space he needed to observe on his own.

Alex was glad she didn't want to talk about his deteriorating medical condition. He was free to first discuss business. "Sam, you know your article that recently came out in New York Magazine?"

"Yes?"

"Well," Alex looked back at her, he felt silly addressing the painting, "there were some comments you made that really intrigued me and I wanted to ask if you could expand upon some of those ideas."

"Of course." Samantha clasped her hands behind her back, settling into the conversation.

Alex shifted slightly to the right so he could compare the painting to its neighbor. It was by the same artist and used similar colors.

"The article focused on how much your employees respect you and how you are able to motivate and inspire them so easily. You in turn mentioned that you set very high standards for your employees, but that they are thrilled to meet them. Why is that?"

"If you remember, I also said that I support them in the achievement of these standards. It's not about setting the bar too high for them to grasp," replied Samantha. "I don't ask them to do anything I wouldn't do myself. They know this, because they've seen me live up to those standards. However, I believe in their capability, and I support them. Even when they make mistakes. It's that belief and support that motivates them to rise to the challenge."

"That makes sense. But if your employees are anything like mine, I'm sure they screw-up occasionally! How do you handle those mistakes or problems when they arise?"

"Are you talking about from an HR perspective or the company in general?"

"Both." Alex moved a few steps on to the next work of art and Samantha trailed behind him.

"For me, the best way to handle any problem is by having a macro view of the situation and that includes viewing the issue as an opportunity instead of a problem."

"So, we're back to the idea of perspective again?"

Samantha smiled. "I guess that's the theme of the day. Yes, that's one way of describing it."

Alex was once again tempted to bend his neck at an uncomfortable angle to look at the sculpture before him, but a soft chuckle near his left shoulder caused him to check that errant idea.

"What comes out of looking at a problem as an opportunity? I mean, I can guess the obvious answer, but I'd rather hear your view on it."

"Gee thanks," remarked Samantha with a sardonic smile. "Part of keeping my team motivated is by being a role model. They are going to feed off my energy and react the way I do. If I get overly stressed and emotional about a problem, then they will learn the wrong way to deal with the problems they come across. However, if I remain objective and look at the problem from every possible angle, then I can soon find the silver lining, as it were. But the key to developing your people is to allow them to make a mistake and find the solution to the problem on their own."

"Do you have an example you can share?"

"Certainly, but first, I want to show you this." Samantha led him over to another painting that looked like something Monet would have created if he had walked the streets of modern day Manhattan.

Alex was relieved he didn't feel the need to "understand" this piece. Samantha stood close enough that he could smell her gardenia based perfume. It fit the springtime season perfectly.

"We had a situation, recently, that included some miscommunication between an artist, one of our galleries and a buyer. There was a mix up with the purchase of a piece that wasn't intended for sale, and tensions were soon running high between everyone. There were multiple ways we could've handled the situation that would have easily covered our asses from a business perspective, but it would have meant losing a valuable employee and potentially a client. We aren't in the business of stroking the egos of our artist, nor can we always afford to make everyone happy."

Samantha sighed slightly, as if the recent stress of the events were still causing the muscles in her shoulder to tighten.

"So," Alex stole a sidelong glance at her. He was right, she did look stressed just talking about it. "What did you do?"

"I saw the situation as an opportunity to increase client relations and install a sorely needed new policy on how to handle the display of artist pieces that were reserved for an upcoming auction. I also believed this would be an extremely valuable developmental lesson for an employee that I believe has potential to advance in her career. In the end we managed to work the wrinkle out and everyone walked away with a satisfactory compromise. That employee helped create an innovative new system which increased business by fifteen percent the following month!"

"Wow."

"Indeed."

"What steps do you find crucial in implementing new systems to solve these problems?"

"Well," Samantha took a deep breath before launching into her reply. "There are certain aspects I feel that are crucial to overcoming any problem and in turn implementing its solution. First, transparent communication is paramount."

"Ah, so you make sure everyone's views are expressed and taken into account?" Alex had been hearing similar responses from many of the business owners he had been recently in contact with during this process. He was really beginning to see how crucial this step was to a successful business.

"Exactly," agreed Samantha. The two of them moved on to another display that featured fifty 4x4 inch wood chips arranged in a neat square. The paint splattered across them didn't look like much of anything until one took several steps back to see the image the colors and varying textures revealed.

"I like this one," Alex chuckled.

Samantha rolled her eyes with a shake of her head, "You haven't changed a bit, have you?" Alex rolled his shoulders up to his ears and grinned. "The female figure is a work of art in and of itself."

Alex blushed like a school boy, "Heh, it sure is." He gulped, suddenly feeling self-conscious. He began to move away from the image, but an insistent tug on his sleeve forced him to stay. Samantha's gaze held no judgment as she glanced at him before returning to her own admiration of the artwork.

"So, transparency is important. What else is do you believe helps motivate or inspire your people? Besides communication?" Alex pressed.

"Having open minded people, which is only possible to obtain through a careful recruitment process."

"Right," Alex's tone encouraged her to continue.

"Showing your employees how to determine the real issue to a problem and removing obstacles is always a big one."

"I'm not sure I follow you on that one. What do you mean *the real issue*?" Alex was intrigued at her response and slowed his pace as he moved to the next display.

Samantha paused as she tried to think of an example that would reiterate her point. "Well, the best way to think about it is like a doctor would when diagnosing a mental illness." Samantha's eyes got larger as she realized how well her example fit the scenario. She continued, "If the doctor just gave you medicine for the problem--let's say, you were getting migraine headaches—and she prescribed a medication to prevent migraines; it may prevent your headaches, but she may have not cured the underlying issue. The underlying issue could have been as easy as asking the right questions to find out all you needed was a new pair of eye glasses!"

"Ha-ha, I see what you mean. Ingenious of you!" Alex smiled and pointed his finger at Samantha.

"Well, there will always be the obvious ones presented in a problem, but then people have a unique knack of throwing their personal ones into the mix. It doesn't matter what solution you offer, there will always be someone who will come up with an objection of some nature."

"Hence the importance of having open minded people on your team."

"See, this is why I like you, Alex. You understand everything has a purpose."

"I learned from the best," he winked at her.

Samantha's mouth fell open in surprise, "Alex Moss are you flirting with me? What's gotten into you?" she grinned.

Alex shrugged, his cheeks turning pink again, "Sorry. I know that was unprofessional of me. I've just had a lot going on lately."

"That I can see. You aren't acting like yourself." Samantha's tone softened, "I'm not complaining, though."

Alex straightened his shoulders, releasing the wound in his pride after realizing it was unnecessary.

"So, other than what you've mentioned, is there anything else you can think of that helps you in this situation?"

"Strategy." Samantha replied pointedly. "Without a solid implementation strategy and follow-up, your new procedures will never be effective. A lot of people get hung up on that. They find a brilliant solution and throw it at the wall, hoping it'll stick without planning for any bumps along the way. They don't consider the "what ifs" nor do they consider the fact that the solution will have to be maintained."

"What do you mean by that?" Alex turned toward Samantha, their circuit of the gallery floor, finally complete.

"What I mean is that systems are a lot like plants. They need constant watering, the right amount of sunlight, and attention. You can't just stick a plant in a pot and expect it to flourish if you never look at it again. Systems are the same way. You have to constantly maintain them, re-evaluate them to ensure they are still serving their intended purpose, and restructure them if and when they need it. They have to be flexible and evolve with your business in the same way your business has to evolve within its industry."

"Huh," Alex was already thinking of several problems and systems within his company that he knew he needed to revisit. "I never thought of it that way before. Interesting."

"I see I've already lost you to visions of grandeur," Samantha smirked. "Well, it was nice seeing you again, Alex. Next time, don't take so long in between visits, hmmm?"

"I'm sorry," Alex sighed with a shake of his head. "I'm being rude. You've given me a lot to think about. And, you're right, it's been too long. I promise it won't happen again." He raised his right hand and held up two fingers, "Scout's honor."

Samantha humphed with a roll of her eyes, but she couldn't help the smile that crept across her face. "But before I go, Samantha there is something we need to talk about…"

———————

Alex leaned toward Samantha to give her an embrace and a soft kiss on the cheek. He left the gallery feeling light hearted and even more at peace than when he walked through the front door. It had been good to see Samantha again. He was really proud of the work she was doing. Anthony was waiting to pick Alex up, the grey saloon was gleaming in the bright light, freshly washed and detailed by his chauffeur.

"The car looks great, Tony!"

Anthony looked slightly taken aback. He was still getting used to the person his employer was becoming. Someone who was more appreciative and encouraging.

"Uh," Anthony cleared his throat, slightly embarrassed by the praise as he opened the car door and Peter slid into his seat. "Thank you Mr. Moss?"

Alex waited until Anthony was settled behind the wheel before he asked, "How is school going for you?"

"Oh, it's...it's great, Mr. Moss. Thank you for writing that recommendation for me."

The car pulled into traffic only to stop in 300 feet at a stop light.

"Excellent. I'm glad to hear it! I've got to make a quick call to Peter and then I want to hear more about it.

"Of course, Mr. Moss."

Alex pulled out his cell phone and dialed his friend's number.

"Hey Peter, how's the little guy holding up?"

"Well," Peter replied, "He still has a small fever, but he's keeping crackers and Gatorade down, so I think we are almost out of the woods."

"Oh, I'm glad to hear it. After you finish taking care of your son, I have another assignment for you."

Without hesitation Peter replied, "Sure, give me a second to grab a pen." Alex waited for a brief moment for Peter to return. "OK, I'm ready, shoot!"

"In addition to the new profit sharing we've set up, I also want to work on some new incentive plans for our employees. Maybe you can get a team together to come up with some ideas on programs that will encourage people to cut costs and increase revenue. Also, we need to develop a better bonus and recognition program for the ones who really make a difference. Nothing that will break the bank...and the rewards may not have to be only monetary. Be creative. We always think the only thing they care about is money. I have a feeling there may be other things we could give them which would motivate them just as much...if not more. What do you think?"

"Absolutely! This sounds great and I know the perfect team to call on for this. They will be excited to get started right away."

"Great! I'm happy to hear that." Alex stretched his long legs before him, thankful for the Rolls' ample backseat legroom. "Oh, and let's run a competition for anyone who can come up with a better term to replace the word "employee." That word sounds so formal. We are building a community, a family and we want our people to feel as if they work *with* us, not *for* us. We are in this together and if this is going to work, we will need every willing and able team member on board with this. A change in terminology is just a start."

"Ok, as long as we don't go the Nestle route."

"The Nestle route?" Alex questioned.

"Yeah, apparently, everyone hugs one another upon greeting, and I do mean everyone."

Alex belted a laugh so loud it caused Tony to slightly jump at the sound. "Ah come on Peter, you afraid to give me a big hug in public or something?" He couldn't help but poke at his best friend.

"OK Alex, baby steps, baby steps. Let's just take it one change at a time."

June 30

To **effectively** run a team, you must develop strong personal relationships with your staff. The personal relationships build a family spirit within your organization.

I've begun to **celebrate** their achievements with them, and when they fail, I feel that a part of me has failed as well.

These **strong personal relationships** keep me going when times get tough and allow me to go to my team when I need them most. Without this emotional connection, there is no good reason for your employees to risk doing whatever it takes to help you become successful.

Ask yourself...

-Why do your employees love to get up and come into the office each morning?

-Why do they love being part of your team?

-What motivates them to work for a common cause?

Create a family atmosphere within your company. Have an annual office picnic. Invite all employees, families and customers to come. Give every child a gift. Get your employees together as often as possible to converse outside of their normal working environment. Build **true friendships** with them, and show them how much you appreciate their efforts.

PART 8

KNOW YOUR CUSTOMER

"Don't find customers for your products, find products for your customers."

Seth Godin

"So, you just stick your bag of laundry in the locker, lock it, and leave?" Peter looked with astonishment at the six new lockers that had been installed in a basement room of his residential building.

"Yup," the Super nodded. "Well, that and you have to place your order for what you want done."

"What do you mean, place my order? It's laundry, how much info do they need?" Peter couldn't help but open and close the metal door. The freshness of the installment was a novelty in a city where so many things were antiques, including most buildings. He liked the crisp snick of the new metal rubbing together each time he closed the door. The sound was barely a whisper one moment, or a clang the next depending upon how much force he used.

Donny, the Super, chuckled as he stuck his thumbs in the belt loops of his navy blue maintenance jumpsuit. "Oh, you'd be surprised at the options available for this service. They don't call it Dash Locker for nuthin'."

"Tell me." Peter now picked up one of the bright blue bags that the company had left for people to place their laundry in. He examined the white company logo on the front with a critical eye. "Load, Lock, Live," the logo proudly exclaimed. *Creative*, thought Peter.

"They have quite the list to choose from when you go online or use their app to place your order. As the Dash Locker chap explained to me you can have them wash your clothes, dry clean them, or even shine your shoes. You can either leave the laundry detergent and dryer sheets you want them to use, or you can ask 'em to use what you want. Then there's always the option of leaving special instructions in the note section of the order form. Your account is connected to your billing info, and well—"he shrugged his broad shoulders. "That's 'bout it."

"That's it?" Peter raised an eyebrow. "What about pick up and turnaround time?"

"Oh yeah," Donny dug around in his pant pockets. He pulled out a wrinkled piece of paper and after fumbling with it for a moment, stretched it between his hands and read its contents. His bottom lip stuck out in contemplation for a few seconds. "Nope, not it." He crumbled the paper in his fist before tossing it onto a nearby table. He dug around in his pockets again. Apparently they were pretty deep as they swallowed his hands up to his mid forearms. Peter tried not to chuckle as Donny rocked from side to side as each hand alternated digging deep within the pockets. He pulled out a few more sheets of paper, some rubber bands, paper clips, a few peppermints, and three pens. All of these items, plus a large tangle of twine were tossed on the nearby table before, finally, he pulled out the right paper.

"Eureka! Heheh, I've always kinda liked that word." Donny waved the piece of paper in the air triumphantly. "It always makes me feel—well—," he struggled for the right thought, "you know?"

"Yeah," Peter tossed the blue bag back into the basket where the others waited. There was another basket next to it that held forest green bags with the same logo. "It makes every discovery of the day feel important. Even the little ones. It's a good way to stay positive."

"Right! Thanks," Donny grinned and Peter nodded back. "Now, according to the receipt, here, the Dash Locker guy left, the clothes for this building will be picked up every morning at 8 and the turnaround is generally 24 hours. Of course, if you have extra requests, that could change the turnaround time. He said some services may take longer than others."

"Huh, that's interesting."

"And get this," Donny leaned forward slightly, as though he were about to reveal a big secret.

Peter leaned forward a little too, ready for the secret.

"Some Dash Locker locations are on demand."

Peter blinked at him in confusion. He was slightly disappointed at the reveal, based on Donny's conspiratorial tone. "That's it?"

"That's it?" Donny repeated incredulously. "Whatdaya mean, that's it? It means that you can drop your things off, place the order and they pick it up right away."

"Oooh," this info was a little more interesting.

"Yeah, some places have specific pick up times, like we do because we only have a few lockers. But the bigger locations will have on demand service."

"Wow, that *is* nice." Peter pursed his lips in thought. He couldn't wait to talk to Alex about this.

Donny nodded in agreement before his walkie talkie attached to his belt squawked. Peter couldn't understand a word that came out that thing. The voice nearly sounded like Charlie Brown's teacher. However, Donny seemed to understand the message, and rattled off a quick reply.

"Well, if ya don't mind Mr. Walker, there's a plumbing issue on 10 I've gotta take care of."

"Let me guess, little Micah Barbour is still flushing his toys?"

Donny chuckled as he waved over his shoulder, he was already halfway out the door. "Ya didn't hear it from me!" he called out.

Peter smiled and shook his head at the retreating figure. He climbed the stairs two at a time, preferring the exercise over using the elevator.

Once back in his apartment he opened his laptop and searched the internet for the Dash Locker website. He spent the next few minutes reading the company's FAQ page and "How it Works" page. Donny was right, this company seemed to have thought of nearly everything. It looked as if they were also working on a package delivery service. For a company that was open 24/7 in a city that never slept, their business was truly innovative.

Peter rubbed his chin thoughtfully, he knew he wanted to present this information to Alex. Alex had called him yesterday to tell him that the next thing he wanted to work on was product differentiation, but he was still trying to decide on a product or service in the area to use as an example. Peter felt sure that this was what they were looking for. He typed a quick text to Alex and after closing the lid to his computer, returned to his morning pre-work habits. He rubbed his hands together as he headed for the kitchen to prepare his favorite morning smoothie.

Alex stifled a big yawn, rubbing his eyes. His lids were heavy with sleep. "Was it really necessary that I meet you here at 2 am?"

"Oh what's wrong, old man?" Peter clapped his friend on the back as he dug in his back pocket for his wallet. "Are you still jet lagged from that mysterious place you're always disappearing to on the jet? I'm going to put a tracker on you someday."

"Ha. The key words there are 'old man.' You know I need my beauty sleep." Alex forced a weak smile, neatly sidestepping the topic once more, as he watched Peter swipe his credit card on the door panel. The front door of the building clicked open and the two friends walked in.

"I won't argue with you there." Peter flashed a playful grin that Alex returned with an eye roll. Peter knew it pick his battles with Alex. If Alex didn't want to give information up, he wouldn't, no matter how hard you push.

Both men paused briefly in the entryway of the room. However, even though it was two in the morning, their New York resident experience quickly kicked back in and they moved out of the doorway's path. The lateness of the hour could never depict when someone would walk through the front door.

The sight that greeted them was rows upon rows of tall black lockers with white numbers painted on, a keypad for the lock, and the company's ostrich logo. There were even corridors made of lockers that the two men could walk down.

"What is this place?" Alex stared in wide eyed wonder at the set-up, much in the same way Peter had viewed the lockers in his building.

"See, this is the great thing about New York." He was leaning casually against a set of lockers. "You can live here for years and still find hidden gems like this one that you never knew about." Peter proceeded to tell Alex about the lockers in his building and related the information of Dash Locker's services and process that he had found online. The entire system was based on convenience and effective, but hands off communication, between client and business. The client would most likely never meet or talk to the people shining their shoes or folding their unmentionables, but that was part of the allure of the business. Busy New Yorkers could hand off a necessary, but time consuming chore and not worry about it being done properly. They could return any time after the company notifies them that their belongings are ready. They are no longer bound by the hours of the dry cleaner or washateria.

"Huh, no kidding." Alex smiled, stuffing his hands in his pockets. "This is genius! I love how they took their 'product' which is actually a service to meet a customer need, and from what I can see exceeded their expectations."

"I know." Peter was still looking at the place in wonder. Clever business ideas always made him giddy. This place was already starting to give him an idea for improving one service Moss Global offered. He knew that convenience was often really important to clients. Some clients prefer a personal touch when it comes to service, but others don't mind sacrificing it, when an automated system can offer the ultimate convenience. Of course, as long as there was a person to call when an issue arose.

"So, how do you think they came up with this idea?" Peter asked. "I mean it's clever, sure, but it is well thought out. When you consider all that they offer, you can tell they attempted to think of everything!"

"Well," Alex leaned his back against one of the lockers and crossed his ankles, "Even without speaking to the founders of the company, I think we can make an educated guess."

Peter nodded for Alex to continue.

"They probably began by looking at the need that customers had. We all know that living in this city often makes laundry a challenge. Not all buildings have laundry services, and then there is the hassle of lugging your stuff down to a dry cleaner or Laundromat. Sometimes it's not all that bad. I mean there's fluff and fold services that will return your laundry to you when done. But, honestly that's really the only convenience these companies offer."

"Right, and then there's the hours. Even though many of them have pretty broad hours, it can still be inconvenient if your availability doesn't match."

"This is true." Alex agreed with another large yawn. "If we're going to continue this discussion, though, I need coffee."

Peter pushed off from the lockers he was leaning against with his right shoulder. He pointed outside, "There's a 24 hour dinner on the corner of this block."

"Done and done. Change approved, let's go."

Peter laughed. He loved the new Alex. Despite his declining health, the man was as upbeat as ever.

Once the two men were settled in a red vinyl booth with steaming cups of coffee set before them, their conversation quickly picked up again.

"You know," Alex rubbed the back of his neck in thought, "I bet, knowing the need and market, they did one of two things. Possibly even both."

"What's that?"

"Well, if you want to create a product or service that is going to exceed expectations you have to look at the competition and survey the market. See how they feel about the options they have. What do they like, what do they not like?"

"And after that?" Peter took a sip of his coffee. A pained look crossed his face and he reached for the sugar packets.

"They probably sat and thought to themselves. What would the perfect service look like? Of course it doesn't exist and whatever they dreamed up may not even be feasible. I'm sure they used the information they got from those surveys to guide them. However, in the end, whatever they dreamed up they used as inspiration."

The clinking of Peter's spoon as it mixed his sugar and coffee punctuated his next words. "So you think they created what they could to get as close to that perfect product as possible?"

"Yeah, I mean based on what you told me, from everything they offer, from the transparency of the info made available on their website, and from the fact that they are working on providing more locations and services—" Alex spread his hands. "—I think it's pretty obvious that they have a bigger goal in mind. And that," Alex tapped the table for emphasis, "is exactly the point of product differentiation."

"What? Striving for perfection?" Peter frowned, worried where this line of reasoning was going to take them. They had worked so hard on taking a step back and scaling things down, but perfectionism would surely ruin all of those advancements.

"Yes and no. The point is you use the perfect product or service as a goal. Even if it's impossible on many levels. Maybe the technology doesn't exist, or there aren't enough hours in the day, or," Alex leaned forward in excitement, his index finger raised, "no one could afford what it would cost to produce. Still it's a benchmark and an inspiration. We have to continue to dream big and not be afraid to innovate. We always have to keep our eye on the competition and--," he brought the raised hand palm down, flat on the table. The slap caused the dishes to rattle under the force of his thump. Peter covered his very full, but freshly doctored coffee.

"—and—," Alex continued. "Watch what they are doing and how the market reacts to them. Then, based on that and the reaction they are having to our product we adjust from there."

"Oh," Peter breathed a sigh of relief. "So, you mean we need to evolve within the industry so we can continue to stand out and be the leaders instead of the followers."

"Yes!" Alex beamed, as he blew on his coffee. "You got it! Of course there's more to it than that."

"There is?"

"Oh yeah. That's just the tip of the iceberg, but it's also the hardest. The rest is defined by the product or services--," Alex ticked off the list by tapping the edge of this spoon against his coffee cup, "functionality, the sensory impact it has, if there are any unconscious associations it can trigger, what purchasing influences are a conscious factor, price, value, access and convenience."

Peter nodded in agreement over the list. "With any product, you could spend all day deciding those details."

"True," Alex raised his mug in a semi-salute to the statement. "However, all of the market research and prep you do, as well as your vision of the perfect product will help guide the rest of those decisions."

"So," Peter wiggled his eyebrows, "Which of our many services are we going to run through this system?

Alex smirked, "I'm glad you asked."

Why do our customers buy? July 16

Understand what your **market** wants by getting to know your customers. Don't guess! Use marketing resources like customer surveys (www.surveymonkey.com), or employ a company to do the research for you.

Knowledge of their needs, wants, and desires is crucial for your ability to conform to their needs.

If you want to **create** a product or service that is going to exceed expectations you have to also understand your competition.

Remember, your brand is in your customers eyes. Understand how your customer see's you and determine if you need to change your brand.

DREAM BIG!!

Evaluate the following for your product or service:

- how well it works to fill need
- customers perceived value for price
- unconscious associations of you and your product
- Purchasing influences such as price, value and convenience.

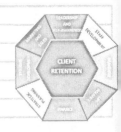

PART 9
CREATING MEANINGFUL
SYSTEMS

*"I choose a lazy person to do a hard job. Because
a lazy person will find an easy way to do it."*

Bill Gates

Alex and Peter stood shoulder-to-shoulder, gazing up at the large window before them. The window contained a fantasy scene worthy of any dream made reality. It looked like a dystopian take on Alice in Wonderland, with the names of the designers whose clothes were fitted on the mannequins proudly displayed as set props.

"Balenciaga" was the leafy part of a tree, "Prada" was a cloud, "Dolce & Gabbana" were the blades of swords. On and on it went, in dizzying intricate detail.

Alex pressed his shoulder against his friend's a little more, thankful that Peter could bear the weight. To anyone passing by it only looked as if the guys were just trying to take up as little space as possible during their wool gathering on a busy walkway. In reality, Alex had gotten weaker. They had already done a lot of revamping at Moss Global and improvements were already seen and felt throughout the company. Even though Alex insisted they still had much to do, they had to postpone their last few meetings. The chemo treatments were not working, and the cancer had now spread into his lungs. The prognosis wasn't good and only a select few had been informed of the news. Alex didn't want to discuss it, his only focus was on the business and transforming it. He still worried about his daughter, Amanda, turning into a workaholic like him and missing out on life. She had gone out on a fourth date with someone she was obviously interested in—and to top it off—Alex even admired. She usually never made it past the second date because she was too busy. For Alex, this turn around couldn't come soon enough.

"Who would have thought to combine the 'Hunger Games' with 'Alice in Wonderland'?" Alex scoffed.

"Hmmm," remarked Peter. "Actually, it's not that far of a stretch, if you think about the symbolism and the structure of—"

"Nope," Alex cut Peter off, "My brain doesn't have enough cells left to even begin to contemplate this"—he waved his hand at the window, "combination. This is the moment your philosophy minor rears its ugly head to bore us all, huh?" Alex chuckled.

"You sound like Emily," Peter smiled, "She hates it when I do that too."

"I value that you're a deep thinker. You just have to remember that it's hard for the intellectual bourgeois like me to keep up."

"Oooh, big words used improperly! You are far from bourgeois, Mr. Private Jet Owner. Or I heard last week, used to be a jet owner. Congratulations I might add."

"Ha! And thank you. But intellectually..."

"Heh, touché."

"Ok, enough of this. Let's go in." Alex straightened up further.

"Are you going to be ok? Bloomingdales is huge, I'm not even sure I want to know how many floors are in this building."

"But it has chairs that I can collapse on if I need to, right?" Alex picked at his white t-shirt that he once filled out. It draped his frame like a tent.

"Sure," Peter scratched his head, it had been years since he set foot into a clothing store. He usually let Emily brave that jungle. She enjoyed it. "I think they're near the fitting rooms?"

"Excellent. We'll make sure we know where they all are and try to stay close."

"Ok," Peter didn't sound convinced as Alex took a few wobbly steps near the front door. Fortunately a young couple opened the door and held it behind them so the two men could walk through. It saved Alex the embarrassment of struggling with it, or Peter from rescuing him from it.

Once inside the first set of doors, the two men were in a circular entryway and they were presented with two choices: One, they could go straight through another set of doors that led them to the women's, children, and home sections. Or two, they could go right, down a flight of steps and into the men's section.

It took them a split second to decide and no words were needed as they turned right and went down the stairs. Alex gripped the silver railing down the middle for support, carefully avoiding the puddle of spilled coffee that was slowly dripping from one stair to the next. When they got to the landing, they were confronted with another choice. Either go down another flight of stairs to the "denim lab" and other "casual" wear or turn to the other set of glass double doors on the left where the rest of the menswear waited.

Alex looked at Peter in exasperation. "Whatever happened to the basics? Shirts, pants, suits and shoes?"

Peter shook his head in agreement, "Nothing is so simple anymore. Where'd Henry say he'd meet us again?

Alex pulled out his phone and after a few quick swipes and taps reached the message he had receive last week from Bloomingdale's menswear director.

"The Michael Kors shop," he announced.

"Well," Peter opened the glass door to their left. "At least I've heard of him. Holy smokes!"

He looked stunned at the magnitude of the options before him. "How are we going to find anything in this place?" He craned his head, looking left and right for a sign that read 'Michael Kors.' He saw the names of several other designers on walls, but none were the right one. The men took a few steps forward before realizing that they were about to enter a maze. This wasn't your typical department store.

Alex was also taking everything in. He noticed a short set of stairs that seemed to lead to a new maze of shops, and other pathways that led to even more displays and sections of designer shoes. Even the labels on the walls with arrows pointing them to different sections were vague.

"Henry wanted to meet at a different shop originally, I think the name was Kent and something or another." Alex sighed, "I don't remember."

At that moment a young man in a three piece dark blue linen suit approached them. "Can I help you gentleman find anything?"

Normally both men would have said "no" and enjoyed the challenge of finding their way. However, they had an appointment to keep.

"Yes," said Peter. "Can you point us in the direction of Michael Kors?"

"Certainly," the young man smiled warmly, "Just go up those stairs, through the undergarment section and keep going straight. You'll see it on your right hand side."

"Got it, thanks!" Peter nodded to the young man and Alex added his thanks.

After the young man walked off Peter eyed Alex warily. "I hate asking, but" he indicated the stairs with a tilt of his head. "Can you handle another flight?"

Alex attempted a smirk, but his skin had blanched further upon the sight of the stairs. "Yep!"

The two men made it up the stairs and quickly shuffled to the side, out of the way of the rest of the shoppers. Alex had to catch his breath and was thankful for the bottle of water he had brought.

"You look like you could use a shot of caffeine."

"More like an IV of espresso. You never appreciate having the energy of even a fifty year old, until it's gone."

"You know, we can do this some other day. We don't have"—Peter was silenced by Alex's hard look.

"Yes we do. Henry has agreed to take time out of his schedule to meet with us, and we have work to do."

Despite Alex's words, the unspoken thought of "we don't have much time left" hung heavy in the air between them.

Without a glance back, Peter stepped back into the flow of the foot traffic that was weaving its way through the undergarment section. Alex followed behind at a slower pace.

Before long they arrived at the Michael Kors shop within Bloomingdales and Alex immediately pulled out a large black ottoman that was tucked underneath a table laden with shirts and pants. He sat down, and surveyed the shop they were in, comparing it to the others around it. It was obvious that each brand had its own identity and each little shop within the big store reflected that. After fending off two eager, but very friendly sales staff, the men were greeted by Henry Morris.

"Good afternoon, gentlemen!" He grasped both men by the hand and after vigorous handshakes, pulled out the other ottoman and sat.

"Hello Henry, thanks for meeting with us on such short notice. I know you only have an hour so I'll get right to the point." Alex folded his hands in his lap, suddenly wishing it was still sweater season as goose bumps dotted his arm.

"Sure," replied Henry.

"Bloomingdales is a big retailer with many locations, and I know that in order for it to function like a well-oiled machine, it needs systems."

"Right," said Henry.

"I was wondering if you could tell me about the evaluation and maintenance of these systems because obviously your company isn't just starting out. At this point, I can imagine you do more evaluation and maintenance over creation."

"You're right," agreed Henry. "A lot of what we do involves regularly scheduled evaluation and if needed, maintenance of systems already in place."

"So what are the steps that your company employs for this process?" Alex asked.

Peter inched a little closer to their tight knit group. He stood with arms crossed comfortably, a look of concentration on his face. Alex had been talking of systems for weeks and they had implemented many new ones. However, they quickly realized that several of the systems that were already in place could use some refurbishing. He wasn't even confident if all of them were working properly. At least two were going to need to be axed for sure.

"Well, one thing to keep in mind when it comes to systems is that they operate in the same way as the systems in our bodies do. We have a nervous system, a lymphatic system, a skeletal system, and organs that work in conjunction. If any of those systems are off, even if they don't directly relate to any of the others, the others are ultimately affected. Just keeping that concept in mind is a great motivator to regularly monitor and maintain the systems that make up our business."

"Can you give us an example of a system that your company uses?" Peter asked.

"Sure," Henry tapped his knee for a moment in thought. "There are so many to choose from! One is our return policy system. It's actually very simple in nature, but very important to our customer service system."

"I've heard really good things about how easy it is to return merchandise to this store." Alex replied.

"I'm glad the word has gotten out, which is precisely the point. We sell high end merchandise and our clients, as people of means to afford those products, have a certain expectation when they make those purchases. One, is ease and convenience in making a return. Every product we sell gets an extra sticker affixed to the product's packaging or tag and on it, is a return code. Many people will lose the receipt for a purchase, but most will hold on to the box it comes in. Because of that, when we attached that sticker, it makes returns easy. The code is then matched to their purchase in the system and we are able to return the product."

"That's a pretty efficient sounding system. But, what if they don't have the receipt or the packaging? What if you don't even know when they bought it?"

"Ah!" Henry raised a finger and momentarily waved it in the air, "I'm glad you asked. If the product is something that is currently in our inventory or has been within the last six months, then we try to work with the person to give them a refund. We can't refund to their card or give them cash, but we can at least offer a store credit."

"Not bad." Peter replied.

"So Henry, let me ask you. Since I'm sure this isn't how Bloomindales' traditional return policy began, can you tell me how this system was evaluated and later improved upon?"

"Absolutely," agreed Henry. "We were getting many complaints from clients about our return policy that was much the same as other stores which meant a 90 day limit and receipt required. So, we looked at our policy and compared it to our competitors. As I said before, ours was very similar, but a few of our competitors were trying out variations on their policies to be more flexible. Part of our process for re-evaluating and fixing this system was to make some slight changes, here and there and monitor the results."

"And?" Peter asked.

"It didn't take long for us to see what worked and what didn't. After that we slowly implemented the plan. We started with a few stores, gave the new system time to work out its kinks and then rolled it out to all of our stores."

Alex nodded thoughtfully, "Well, you've certainly given us a lot to think about. We have several systems in our company that we are thinking of re-hauling."

"Not to mention the new ones we just implemented," suggested Peter.

"Right. We definitely don't want our new systems to fail before they've started."

"Well, gents, I'm glad I was able to help." Remarked Henry. "I'm sorry I haven't been able to give you guys more time."

"Are you kidding?" Alex shook Henry's hand once more. "We are extremely grateful for your time. Thank you."

"It was my pleasure," Henry stood up, and shook Peter's hand as well. "Tell Sarah, that her next personal shopping experience has a 40% discount waiting for her."

"Wow, thanks! She'll be happy to hear that!" Peter beamed, excited to deliver the news and even more grateful that Bloomingdale's personal shopping service prevented him from getting lost in their wondrous but dizzying maze.

Design a Sales System   August 18 ✓

What are your current systems?

Don't wing it, take the time to develop systems now. Failure to create systems early on will make it difficult to implement in the future.

Systems are necessary for training new people. You can't expect employees will "read your mind"

"Training by fire" or as they go is for rookies and amateur's. You are running a business and are the leader of the organization. That doesn't mean you have to have all of the answers or systems in place...but recognize the need and take the time to develop the systems now.

It can be overwhelming trying to do it all at once. Do one at a time. Get your staff involved and create systems for their position when appropriate.

Create benchmarks for success. What is the system supposed to do and how will you know if it is working or not?

Steps to Create a System: ✓

1 - **Identify the problems first.** Systems should be designed to resolve problems, create ease of use and identify opportunities. Most of the "issues" in your office are problems due to the lack of a system.

2 – What is the **economic impact** of each problem? ✓ Choose to correct the easy ones first and the ones that are costing your company the most if left unresolved.

3 – Make sure you are **correcting the problem** and not treating the symptom! What is the real problem?

4 – **Document** what type of system would resolve the issue and illustrate before implementing.

5 – **Create the System** with the help of employees. Look for automation first! Before creating, always check to see if the system or process exists and can be purchased more affordably than developing your own.

6 – **Implement the System**

7 – **Check the System**

TYPES OF SYSTEMS

* Marketing Systems

Important!!

Create 4 Active and 4 Passive Marketing First Contact Script

* Use Sales Presentation to Meet with Client in-person

    Differentiate yourself, and your product!

* Product Delivery Systems - deliver product and exceed customer expectations!

* Client Retention Systems - Create re-contact program and cross-sell

* Referral Systems

* Recruiting Systems

* Employee Review Systems

PART 10
BUILT TO IMPRESS SALES

"It is your responsibility to make the client like you. If they like you, they will listen. If they listen they will believe. If they believe, they will buy."

Zig Ziglar

"**T**he gentle sound of the Hudson River's waves, slapping against the hull of his boat, the distant cry of the gulls outside and the soft rocking was making Alex sleepy. His lids fluttered open and shut heavily as he stared at the screen of his iPad propped up on his custom teak writing desk. Alex took in a deep breath. He had only been up for a few hours and even though he got good sleep last night, his energy never lasted long. He hated it. He was used to having only two speeds. Turbo and hibernation. Now his body seemed permanently stuck in second gear no matter how much rest he got. It was infuriating.

A ringing tone caused him to jerk awake in his chair. Had he fallen asleep? He looked at the sexton shaped brass clock on his desk, but the time wasn't helpful in answering his question. The screen in front of him was telling him that Peter "would like to FaceTime." Rubbing the sleep out of the inner edge of his left eye with one finger he used another to swipe at the screen to answer. Soon, Peter's beaming face filled the screen.

"Hey, Sleepy!" he joked. Peter had been in Texas for the past week visiting Emily's family as they celebrated her grandmother's 90th birthday. It was a well-deserved family vacation that Alex was glad he didn't have to beg Peter to take. "Did I wake you?"

"Um," Alex hemmed, "No, no, I was just working." Alex's swollen eyes and the sleepy sound of his voice gave him away as he stifled a yawn. He really wanted to give a good stretch like a cat on a lazy Sunday, but felt as though that would be pushing it.

"Yeah, yeah, ok," Peter chuckled. "So, remember how we're going to discuss 'Built to Impress Sales,' next?"

"Is that what it was? Uh, yeah I believe so," answered Alex as he tried to clear the cobwebs from his mind.

"Good, check this out!" Peter lifted out of his seat slightly and turned around. He was wearing a purple shirt that had the word 'Buc-ees' on the front and a picture of a cartoon beaver and the phrase 'My overbite is sexy,' on the back.

"My overbite is sexy?" Alex laughed. "What is this?"

"Ha! Have you ever driven through Texas?"

"Driven? Well no, I've only flown into Dallas and San Antonio for some conferences and when the Knicks played the Spurs, but that's about it. Why?"

"Oh man!" Peter groaned. "You are missing out!"

"Really?" Alex's lip curled, "I thought Texas was mostly flat with lots of concrete."

"In a lot of parts, yeah, but that's not the point. The point is this convenience store and gas station that is must see here!"

"A gas station?" Alex was starting to feel bad for being so cynical, but he wasn't sure where Peter was going with this. Still his enthusiasm for this purported Mecca was contagious.

"Get this," Peter leaned closer to the camera in excitement. "When the owners, Arch Aplin and Don Wasek started the company in 1982, they wanted to cater to the families traveling to Lake Jackson, Freeport and Surfside Beach for vacations. They were really smart about it too. If you think about it, when you have a car full of kiddos and you're on your way to your family vacation at the lake or beach, what's the worst part about the drive?"

"The kids whining to use the rest room every five minutes and wanting to know if we are 'there yet'?" Alex rubbed his temples at the thought. This was a torment no parent could ever forget.

"Exactly," Peter snapped his finger at the point made. "However, if you create a gas station and convenience store that exceeds the market's expectations then you've created a product and service that people will seek and hold out for. I mean these guys created a cult following. Would you have ever expected me to wear a shirt like this?"

Alex laughed, "No, I can't say I could have ever seen that!"

"This place is so well known around here is has become THE place to stop on road trips that kids can be encouraged to hold their pee and parents are willing to eke out the last bits of fume from their gas tanks just to make it there. No other gas station convenience store can compare to this!"

"Ok, ok, but it's still a gas station that has bathrooms. I don't see the point and what do you mean 'cult' following?'"

"For starters they have the nicest bathrooms imaginable, far surpassing your typical convenience store. In fact, the bathrooms at their New Braunfels location were voted best in the country. That means they beat out places like…oh, I dunno," Peter waved his hand in the air trying to think of the other locations known for their gleaming throne rooms. "Ah, yes, I read it in an article. It was the restrooms at the Hollywood Bowl and some luxury Chicago Hotel."

"Wow, now that's a great idea! A convenience store that you are not afraid to walk in the restroom in fear of catching something," remarked Alex.

"I know! But that's not all."

"No, I suspect not. Alright, I can see you bouncing in your seat, what else?"

"These!" Peter shoved a cellophane bag at his camera, filling Alex's screen with the image of a bag bearing the same beaver icon and filled with round light yellow puffy pieces of food.

"What. Are. Those?"

Peter was shoving handfuls of the food in his mouth as he looked at the label and then held the bag up to the camera once more, tapping at the name.

"Beaver Nuggets?" Alex laughed.

"Yeah," Peter said around a mouthful of the treats. He mercifully swallowed before continuing. "These things are like little pieces of puffy caramel heaven. Like pieces of a caramel cloud or something. I'm telling you, man! The food here…so good! That's what makes this place so special. They have a full service deli where you walk up to a computer screen, place an order and your food is ready in minutes. You can order lots of different fudges, Dippin' Dots, a variety of jerky and sausages, their own brand of treats like these Beaver Nuggets and then there's the kitsch."

"Oh do tell!" Alex smirked.

Peter had shoved another mouthful of the nuggets down and his next answer sounded sticky. "Like any good Texan company, they take their Texas pride to the max, which is so much fun. Here they have clothing, nick-knacks for the home and kitchen, custom barbeque pits, stuff for the kids, toys, jewelry, things to appeal to hunters and fishers, the list goes on. Oh, and of course the t-shirts and other 'beaver' accessories. Alex, the store in New Braunfels is 68,000 square feet, has 120 gas pumps, 83 toilets, 31 cash registers, 80 fountain machines and to top it all off, every time you walk in the store, you are greeted by a smiling employee!"

"That sounds incredible! I can understand why parents and their kids make it part of their trip. You know people are going to wear your brand proudly and give you a bit of free advertising."

"Right, speaking of which, their billboards that you see leading up to their locations are hilarious. Here, I wrote down a few."

Alex heard the rustling of paper as Peter shuffled through whatever was on his desk. "Ah, here we go. Listen to these." Peter struggled to read off what he wrote through his chuckles, "'Your throne awaits. Fabulous Restrooms.' And 'Only 262 miles to Buc-ee's. You can hold it.' Ha! 'Homemade Fudge. Beaver tested, beaver approved.' Or "Restrooms you gotta pee to believe.' That's all I managed to write down, but I know there's more."

Alex chuckled as he started to wake up. "Those are clever!"

"I'm telling you, in terms of building their sales to impress, these guys blew it out of the water! They knew that all customers are going to have a preconceived notion about a product. They took that notion, factored in the desires and needs of their market, and exceeded expectations. And, even though gas stations and convenience stores aren't that glamorous, they still treat their company as if it offers a luxury and exclusive experience. Which even though, everything isn't lacquered in gold and crusted in diamonds, it still provides an experience you can't get anywhere else. While Emily and the boys walked around the store to look at all of the Texas souvenirs, I asked a few customers why they stopped at Buc-ee's. And believe it or not, the clean restrooms was the first thing out of their mouth…but several followed it up by saying it was because they didn't have to wait. They don't have to wait to get gas, use the restroom, order food or even wait in a line to check out. It's a convenience store that actually brings back the word 'convenience!'"

"I'm really glad you found this place, and told me about it, Peter. Great job. I wasn't sure which company to look at for our sales model, but you nailed it. It sounds like this place understands customers' perceptions, how to make an impression, and how to exceed expectations. If the guys at Buc-ee's can be creative enough to make a convenience store fun, it should be easy for us to find ways to do the same in internet marketing. Thanks for calling and telling me about it."

"Of course," answered Peter, "if I have to suffer through the nicest bathrooms in the country and these delicious Beaver Nuggets, it's a sacrifice I'm willing to make!" He gave a mock sigh.

"Oh good," Alex drawled, "Hey, before I let you go, you guys are coming home tomorrow, right?"

"Right."

"Great, I'm going to send you an email with the details, but after you get your ideas written down about our new sales and marketing strategy, I would like us to focus on another area of the business."

"Sounds great, which one?"

"I need you to work with accounting once more and look at the company's profits and revenue. I want to take 25% of our earnings, after we've taken care of necessary expenses and our employees, and look for ways to get involved in the community by giving back. We should have a ready list of charities that we can give to on a regular basis. Two of my favorites are Kiva and StandUp. We should encourage our employees to suggest some organizations that they are passionate about as well so we can get them involved."

"Not a problem. I've never heard of those two charities. What do they do?"

"Kiva is a charity that allows givers to fund small business owners in third world countries. Even a gift of $25 can help someone start their own business and become self-sufficient. It is beautiful to see these people accomplish their dreams and to see the pride in their faces at owning and running their own business."

"Wow, that's interesting, I like that!" Peter grinned.

"It fits perfectly with our new company goals of building a business that provides happiness rather than indentured servitude! StandUp for Kids is another nationwide organization that gives assistance to homeless teens so they can prepare for adulthood and fend for themselves. The foster care system lets them down terribly, over 100,000 kids are sold into the sex trade industry every year, and if one were to take all of the homeless teens and put them in one city it would be the 7th largest city in the US."

"Those are some scary numbers." Just then, Ben jumped up into his father's lap and Peter gave him a huge hug, kissing him on the top of his curly hair.

Alex looked longingly at the scene on his iPad of his best friend spending time with his family. "Look at how big he's getting! They grow up so fast!"

"Hi Uncle Alex!" Ben shouted in to the screen.

Before Alex could answer, Ben was already off to jump in the back seat and buckle in. "Well, safe travels tomorrow, Peter and I'll see you when you get in, but only if you promise to bring me a bag of those Beaver Nuggets!" Alex's smile was strained, but he was hoping his joke would be enough to deflect the look of regret about the time he had lost with his own children.

The worried twist of his friend's lips told him he wasn't convincing enough, but Peter had enough grace not to say anything.

"Are you kidding me? I'm bringing an entire suitcase of that stuff home! I love you man, take care of yourself!"

Alex smiled, he had been reminding Peter he loved him and valued his friendship for months, and Peter was finally accepting it as truth.

"I love you too, friend."

You must develop systems that blow the socks off of your customers' expectations! Your customer expects that you meet their needs. Give them more than they expect and show them the value for doing business with your company.

Like it or not, before you approach a target customer, they have a preconceived idea about who you are and what it is you have to offer.

No matter what product or service you are offering, you should approach it as if it is a luxury product. You provide the best of what the business has to offer. Just because it isn't the most expensive or lacquered in gold, does not mean it is unworthy of exclusivity. Any product or service worth having, such as yours, is worthy of such an experience.

Part of what you are giving people is a complete experience, something that they have never had before and believe me, they have tried other options in the past. However, they have never come across a product or service like yours before.

First Impressions—

Is the office clean?

Are your employees' professional, fun spirited, full of energy and eager to help?

Is your sales packet professionally printed?

Does it explain what makes you different from your competitor down the street?

Do you know what makes you different from your competition?

In the end, facts really don't matter, but perceptions do.

Predispositions- Culture, Values, Beliefs, Life Events

First Impressions- Media Word of Mouth, Awareness

Reinforced-More of the Above, Positive Sales

First Experience- Demos, Trials, First Sales, Product Use

On Going-Feedback, Repeat Use/Purchases

Overcome with Research-Comparable Markets, Product Strategy

Deliver on our promise

PART 11
BALANCE – THE KEY TO YOUR SUCCESS

"When I went to school, they asked me what I wanted to be when I grew up. I wrote down 'happy.' They told me I didn't understand the assignment and I told them they didn't understand life."

John Lennon

"Here we are, One-o-ninth, and Amsterdam," announced Anthony as he pulled next to the curb.

"Great, thanks Tony!"

"Sure, Mr. Moss. What time do you want me to pick you up?"

As the car came to a stop, Alex undid his seat belt, and began shoving his wallet and phone into his pockets. He could see Peter up ahead, surrounded by shopping bags.

He squinted, trying to make out what his friend was up to.

"Honestly, I'm not sure, Tony. I don't know what Peter's up to this time. He's being secretive." He grabbed the door handle. Normally Tony would open the door for him, but Alex insisted he stopped doing that long ago. He only kept Tony around because, not only had he become such a good friend, but he also wanted to help him out financially before he started school full time in a few more weeks.

"How about I text you when I'm ready?"

"Sounds good Mr. Moss." Tony bobbed his head in agreement.

As Alex approached Peter the items in the bags became clearer. Some contained small paper lunch bags—clearly full—while others contained blankets, pillows, jackets and toiletry kits.

"Wow, what is all this?"

Peter turned to look at the bodega behind him, peering in its windows. "They should be almost done."

"Who? What's going on?"

"Don't worry, don't worry," Peter waved Alex off. "I'll explain once everyone joins us."

"Everyone, who's everyone?" Alex intoned, crossing his arms.

Within a few moments, a group of six, came out of the store blowing on coffees and teas and cracking open breakfast tacos, or peeling apart small pastries. It only took Alex a few moments to recognize the small group as Moss Global employees.

After greeting everyone and quickly catching up, Alex turned to Peter, "So?"

Peter grinned, "So..." the others gathered around, awaiting instruction. "As everyone here knows, we are just one group of twelve that have gathered at different parts of the city, with one mission." Peter pointed to the bags at his feet. "To serve the community. I have an envelope for each of you--," he handed envelopes out to everyone, including Alex. "In each envelope you will find an assortment of gift cards to local eateries around the city."

Alex checked his envelope, and sure enough there were about twenty gift cards stacked together inside.

Peter continued, "As great as it is to serve in the soup kitchens and shelters, not every person who is in need will be able to make it to those locations for a variety of reasons. And if they can't come to us, we are going to go to them!"

Excited murmurs of agreement rumbled through the crowd.

"Everyone should pair up, so we can carry more between ourselves, grab bags and make sure every person you come across, in need, gets one of everything. Any questions?"

The group shook their heads, and began to pair up, chattering amongst themselves and gathering bags.

Peter elbowed an astonished Alex, "so partner, what da-ya say? I brought the kids' old wheelbarrow so we wouldn't have to carry bags. Think you got enough energy to hang with us for a bit?"

Alex snorted, happily, "Are you kidding me? This is great. I don't care if I have to roll myself down the street, I'm in!"

Peter laughed, "I thought as much! Man," he shook his head, "now, that'd be a sight."

After loading bags into the wheelbarrow, Peter and Alex set off down the street, hoping to get some distance from the already dispersing group. They wanted to cover as much territory as possible. It wasn't long before they came upon a war vet who was starting to settle down for the night beneath the scaffolding and in the alcove of one building. He even used the inlets of the wall next to him as shelves to put his belongings, and he had a small radio next to him, playing classical music. His dog and companion 'Lucky' seemed content to lie next to his trusted owner who obviously took great care of him. Over the course of the next 20-minutes, Alex and Peter go to know the Vietnam War Hero and Staff Sergeant whose feet were so swollen he couldn't walk or wear shoes. He told them a little of his story, and they shared the items they had. Since he already had blankets, pillow, and a still intact jacket, he requested they hand those to someone who was in need, but gladly accepted the food and toiletries with profuse thanks.

Alex and Peter said their goodbyes, thanked him for his dedicated service and continued down the sidewalk.

"It took all I had not to cry when he was telling his story about losing his home and family when he returned from the war--," Alex got choked up at the end of the sentence and had to stop.

"I know, I felt the same way. And to wonder how many times we probably walked right by him without as much as a smile. It just doesn't seem right."

"How long have you been doing this?"

"Every two weeks for the past few months," answered Peter. "You remember how you asked me to set up some charities with the company's left over funds after expenses?

"I do."

"Well, Kim in Marketing mentioned how we have a huge need right here in Manhattan, and she suggested that if we combined company wide donations with the extra expenses, then we could do this on a regular basis. We had accounting crunch the numbers and once they gave us the green light, we started. At first there was just a small group of four, but word quickly spread at the office and now we have twelve groups of six! I think we may be adding another next time."

"Peter, that is amazing. And you organized the whole thing?"

Peter shrugged as they approached a young man with a sign, hoping to sell his drawings to earn money. "I did some, but a lot of others pitched in. Overall, it's been a company-wide effort."

Alex's face felt like it was going to split he was grinning so hard after Peter's last statement. His heart felt as if it would burst with pride and joy over what his employees were doing for the people of New York. "That is music to my ears."

Alex and Peter spent another fifteen minutes talking to the young man about his art and how he ended up where he was. Although he didn't volunteer many details, it was clear the teenage boy was a runaway. They gave him a bag filled with everything and bought two pictures each before continuing on their way.

Alex shook his head as he looked at the art in his hands. "These are incredible. I'm going to send a picture to a friend of mine who knows art. These should be in a gallery!"

"Knows art, huh?" Peter winked at Alex with a smirk, "Any day now, I'm still waiting to hear about this mysterious 'art lover.' Please tell me that's where you've been sneaking off too, right?"

Per usual, Alex ignored Peter's prying as he snapped photos with his phone of the drawings before sending a text.

"I'm genuinely impressed of the progress you've made with our company, Peter. I seriously believe you have done more in the past 4 months for employee morale and for community outreach than I've been able to do in 20 years."

"Oh, come on man! You can't be serious."

"I am Peter, I am. Really, I'm very proud of you."

Peter shook his head at Alex's neat change of the conversation. "Well, I think we have both learned a huge lesson over the past few months. The only way we can achieve happiness through our jobs is to have balance our lives. Part of that is giving back to the community and being socially responsible—"

"And community is important to you," Alex added, remembering the conversation they had at the restaurant at the beginning of their little revolution.

"You got it," Peter agreed. "But also, I've realized as I've looked back at both of our lives, that if we don't balance our hard work with taking time to be present and available to our family, getting the rest we need to maintain our health, or enjoying our hobbies and passions, then we run ourselves into the ground. We become useless to our families *and* our business."

"Very true," Alex nodded as they waited to cross the street, they could see another huddled figure laying in the doorway of a building ahead of them. "I just wish I would have realized all of this earlier. I've been trying not to get dragged down into the 'shoulda, woulda, coulda' pit...if you know what I mean?"

"Ha, yeah, it's like a tar pit of regret!"

"It really is!" Alex explained, "ever since I found out about the cancer, I keep running past events through my mind, cringing at my ignorance. I can't believe I let so many opportunities with my family and friends pass me by because I had my head stuck in the sand of my business. I truly thought that if I sacrificed the time, then I would be able to make it up *when* I was successful—I kept thinking...any day now. However, that never happened and I lost everything."

"Alex, you may have sacrificed a lot, but you've changed a lot of lives in the process," Peter pointed out. "We all have regrets and it doesn't do anyone any good to beat ourselves up over the things we've done or didn't do. Sure, you and I could have done more. But instead of focusing on what you didn't do, just think for a minute about the things you did do." They both continued on their slow walk as Alex looked down in deep thought. "There are seriously a dozen people walking around the city of New York handing out food and clothing, on their own time, because you gave them the opportunity to work. Just think about that for a minute Alex."

Alex and Peter crossed the street, dodging their fellow pedestrians and making sharp maneuvers with the wagon. The old wheels squealed in protest and the metal clanged as they pulled it up the ramp.

"I never realize how valuable sleep was until I was forced to sleep through exhaustion," remarked Alex.

"And I can't believe I missed out on Boy's Sunday Funday, for as long as I did," Peter sighed. "I know I have awhile before they leave for their own lives one day, but still. That's time I can't get back."

"And it sure flies by fast."

"You know…" Peter paused for a moment and wanted to ask Alex a question, but didn't know how. "I know we don't talk about 'your condition' much Alex and I know how you hate talking about it." Alex turned to look at his friend and could tell he was struggling to find the right words. "But I've seen a side of you over the past few months that I haven't seen for a long time." Alex looked down and nodded in agreement. Peter continued and tried to elevate the conversation to a positive tone, "I'm certain you are going to beat this, and just wanted you to know that I've really enjoyed getting to see my old friend again."

As Alex continued to lean against the wrought iron fence and stare at the grass beneath his feet, he rubbed at the tightening muscles around his heart. Looking at Peter he said, "I know I haven't been the best of friends to you Peter and I'm truly sorry." Peter looked away and put his hands in his pockets. "And thank you for not disagreeing with me!" They both laughed. "I just see things differently now. When we met in the park for the first time a few months back, I remember seeing the beautiful sunrise and wondered why I stopped paying attention. At that very moment, I realized that I only had so many sunrises left. Even though I haven't been able to see all of them, I try to make it a point to greet the morning and see God's miracle work and remind myself it is a new day. Tomorrow is over and is only a memory. We can't change our past so we can't allow things that have happened, however bad they may have been, to interfere with our happiness. And when the sun sets, I reflect back on the day to think about what I've accomplished. How have I used this incredible gift of life that I have been given? You see, most people live that way. They just live day-by-day, taking life and the people around then for granted. The sunsets, the trees, the air we breathe and even the loved ones around us…we just assume they will always be there. It's crazy really. Even last night when Carly and I were having dinner, I noticed a family of four sitting together but all on their cell phones texting or doing God knows what. I wanted to just walk over and smack the father on the head and tell him what he was missing. I thought, who could be on the other end of that phone could be more important than the people sitting at that table? I wish there were a way I could wake the world up and give them the same message."

Both paused for a moment as Peter let the thought of the message sink in. "Well, you may not have told the world, but you have told me. I know I've been guilty of that more times than I care to count." Peter still hadn't quite forgiven himself for the lack of attention and focus he had placed on his children. He had been spending a lot more time with his family over the past few months thanks to the adjustments he and Alex had been making at the company. Despite the improvement, though he still felt as he had a lot of time to make-up and could see how quickly his boys were growing.

Balance

Maintain a balanced lifestyle is healthy, good for your family and great for your business. You will have the same results, if not better, if you learn to relax, spend quality time with your family and take the time to enjoy life.

Ask yourself...

-Do you get tired during a normal workday?

-After a hard day's work, do you feel as if it takes all you have just to stay awake on your commute home?

You will become **more productive**, have a clearer mind and will **sleep better** if you eat the right things and spend at least 30-45 minutes a day doing some type of exercise. It is a fact that feeling good about yourself will give you more energy, keep you motivated and will help you keep a positive mental attitude.

✳ Ways to stay healthy:

-Cut back on caffeine

-Get 7-8 hours of uninterrupted sleep

-Eat a healthy breakfast

-Eat a lunch outside of the office to get re-energized and re-focused

-No candy jars at the office, places bowls of healthy snacks and foods around.

—Create a relaxing before bed routine. No news or work. Take a hot bath. Wind down. Relax.

—Exercise! Find an alternative stress that works for you and that you love, don't do it as a chore or obligation.

Make an appointment with yourself and take some time every day to relax. Even if it is just for thirty minutes, make some quiet time to recharge your batteries and meditate.

Give yourself permission to relax.

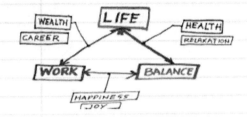

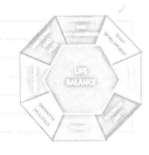

Part 12

Following the Right Financial Path

*"Money is not the goal. Money has no value.
The value comes from the dreams money helps
achieve."*

Robert Kiyosaki

"Wow, what a great performance!" said Peter as he Alex and Carly slowly filed out of the circular auditorium of the Frederick P. Rose Theater at Lincoln Center. They stood shoulder to shoulder with the rest of the crowd and the air buzzed with the excited chatter of the audience discussing the jazz trio they just heard. A few small steps were taken and then a pause as people waited for the rows of seats in front of them to empty. It was a slow process, but most people who too busy laughing and talking with friends and family to mind.

"You should take Emily next time." Remarked Alex, his arm looped with Carly's for support.

"I'd love to, but she really isn't into jazz. I took her here to a ballet performance for her birthday last spring. That was more her style."

"Oh! Was it for 'Jewels'?" asked Carly as they shuffled forward a few more steps. Fifty more steps and they could break free from the herd.

"Yeah, it was. Did you see it?"

"I see it every year. Its spectacular," breathed Carly. Her eyes went a little dreamy while reminiscing.

"Oh, it's every year?" Peter asked. He stood on Alex's other side. As capable as Carly was, he wasn't quite sure the young lady could hold Alex up if he got too weak to walk. He still seemed to be doing a lot better with this new treatment, but a fall last week and his ensuing concussion had everyone on edge.

"You could say it's a bit of a staple for the ballet community."

"I see," nodded Peter.

"I prefer the opera." Alex announced.

"Ok 'Random Man,'" laughed Peter before biting down on a curse. An elderly woman he had paused to allow to step out of her row, had accidentally stamped her cane down on his foot.

"It's not that random, they have opera here."

"Well of course," scoffed Peter as they slowly inched forward once again. Twenty more steps. He could almost taste freedom! "They have it at the Met, but not in this building."

"Oh yeah, in this building," Alex smirked at him. "Didn't you hear?"

"I guess not. Enlighten me then," Peter patted his friend on the back.

"Remember The New York City Opera House?"

When his question was met by Peter's blank stare, he turned to Carly, but shook his head at her. "No you're too young, you wouldn't remember."

"Actually," Carly cleared her throat. "My parents were season ticket holders. However, the opera house claimed bankruptcy in 2013."

"Exactly!" Alex was pleased she was up to speed. The trio finally broke free of the crowd that surrounded them and made their way into the The Mica and Ahmet Ertegun Atrium.

"Now," continued Alex as they dodged groups of people across the merlot carpeted floor. His chief aim was the large wall of windows that displayed a breathtaking view of Columbus Circle and the Midtown Manhattan Skyline. "The New York Opera Renaissance group has taken over and will be reopening the opera house with performances taking place in this building next year."

"Really?" Peter arched a brow. "Aren't they worried about competition from the Met Opera House?" The opera house in question was a few blocks away from their location, but no one could forget its grandeur and formality. The Rose Theater and its fellow theater halls in the Columbus Center were no less luxurious with clean lines, warm colors and large Romare Bearden collages. However, when compared to the Met's art deco chandeliers and fixtures, white marble and bright red carpets, the distinction between the two settings was obvious.

"I wondered that myself," agreed Alex. "Even though both locations have a distinctively different feel, I believe both programs will reflect their venues. It won't be a matter of whose is better, it will be a matter of style and preference. Just like some people may prefer modern art over the work of the Renaissance."

"I read," replied Carly, "that there is a little controversy over hiring Michael Capasso as General Manager for the new opera house. His own opera house, Dicapo, faced a lot of financial difficulties over the past few years."

"Oh," Peter sucked in his breath as the three of them gazed at the glittering view of the city. "That doesn't sound too good, but I'm sure there is more to the story than that. We all know that business and finances are never quite so simple."

"You're exactly right, Peter." Alex stifled a yawn and then crossed his arms over his chest. It wasn't that late, but he was already longing for his bed and the gentle rocking of the waves under his home, the boat. "I was curious too, because that is the next item I want to work on at Moss Global—finances. Remember Roy Niederhoffer from school?"

Peter paused, narrowing his eyes in thought, "Oh yeah, he graduated two years after we did. Wow, what an impressive guy. He founded his own hedge fund in the mid 90's that he's still President of and is a pioneer in multi-asset-class quantitative trading."

Alex smiled, "Now, if you were going to have someone revive a city treasure like the New York City Opera, once called the "People's Opera" can you think of anyone better to helm its board?"

"He's heading the board? Well, if he believes in Capasso, then I don't think the naysayers have any grounds to stand on." Peter remarked.

"Well, Carly was kind enough to arrange a phone meeting with him the other day and I asked him about that. He said that Dicapo Opera was hit by the economic downturn of 2008, but they never stopped filling seats or successfully putting on shows. Even one of their largest creditors the Local 802, continued to perform with them and wrote a letter of recommendation for both the NYCO Renaissance and Mr. Capasso."

"What did Mr. Niederhoffer say about how the new opera house is going to maintain its financial stability," asked Carly. "I'm sure it's something that's on everyone's minds right now."

"I asked him about that," replied Alex, "and he mentioned that the board was going to work together to ensure that they had a clear financial plan and that part of that plan was by continuing the New York City Opera's innovative approach to opera. See, what Roy understands as a businessman is that you have to know your clientele. This can be achieved through market research that we've discussed before and making sure your brand speaks to their needs. However, he did mention that having a season that shifted comfortably between nostalgia and innovation which would speak to his market was not enough. He knows that having a higher percentage of earned income is crucial and that it should be dependent upon the quality of their season and support from secure financial backers, not fundraisers. He is well aware of what didn't work for the last company and what did."

Integrity

Like anything else, you have to have a plan for a destination to get where you are going. Although your budget will not show you the future, it will help you stay on track. A budget will show you if your vision is realistic. The budget is responsible for guiding you to move towards your goals.

Accuracy is important. Creating a routine to forecast what you're up against that might affect your finances is crucial to your success. You have to recognize the "what if's" that might occur during the upcoming months.

There is no magic formula to budgeting and forecasting. It's not designed to be perfect. It's an educated guess based on current facts and history that guide your judgment. Creating your budget is the art of designing a plan to meet your vision in reverse. You are guiding your business each step of the way to obtain the necessary steps that ultimately meet up with your vision. It also ensures you have a way to measure the effectiveness of your plan, so you can make course corrections along the way. It will give you the information you need to make management decisions to keep the staff engaged and on track.

Budget for your company's vision. Budgeting needs to be done once a month and managed as the plan adjusts or foresees a change. Feel free to delegate out budgeting work after creating a plan.

Create a process. Set-up a schedule with deadlines for reporting, time for planning and forecasting, and most importantly, time to manage and review the frequent changes the world brings.

Budget management is what leads to action. The budget decides what you need to achieve, and the variance tells you what happened. When you see the red flags, meaning unexpected issues, you might need to make adjustments. This is how you know where to focus your attention.

Try focusing on your revenues and profits to help achieve your vision:

-Set up specific deadlines to achieve specific goals.

-Create monthly goals for revenue and profits.

-Track your performance. Have them increase each month slightly to meet the checkpoints necessary as you drive towards the vision for your business.

-Calculating the profit goals first so you will know what to expect as far as revenue goals.

-Use your current income statements and expenses as your guides.

How to Calculate Sales Revenue:

Step 1 — Verify Selling Price.

Step 2 — Identify Number of Units Sold

Step 3 — Multiply the selling price of each unit by the total number of units sold.

Step 4 — Add the revenue generated by each product.

PART 13
LIVE WITH NO REGRETS

"Remembering that you are going to die is the best way I know to avoid the trap of thinking you have something to lose. You are already naked. There is no reason not to follow your heart."

Steve Jobs

The reds and oranges thrown by the setting sun glimmered off the glass of the skyscrapers reaching up into the horizon. Even though Manhattan would see the sun again in about ten hours she wasn't going out without a grand finale. In this case, Peter thought the sun looked as if she was holding onto the edges of those buildings for dear life while simultaneously sucking out all the color around her. Manhattan was already fighting back in its scrappy way with neon lights becoming brighter as the sky got darker.

Peter was never more acutely aware of the world around him and his city than in this moment. He was walking down the docks at the harbor, heading towards Alex's ostentatious, but beautiful Azimut Grand yacht. Peter snickered to himself with a small shake of his head as his fingers tightened around the small wrapped packaged gripped in his fingers. Alex never liked calling his boat a "yacht." It was a "sailboat" or just "the boat." The term "yacht" seemed too pompous to Alex.

Peter's throat tightened and he concentrated on the steady thud of his feet against the planks of the dock as the boat in question came into view. Just like the sun, the world—his world—was going to be a little less bright in many ways without Alex. Today was Alex's 50th birthday, and even though it was a day of celebration, it didn't feel like it to Peter. Over the last few weeks Alex had quickly taken a turn for the worse. The new treatment that everyone thought was setting him on the path of recovery had plateaued and he quickly declined. Alex finally put his foot down about the matter and just asked to spend his last few days at home. However, since he had asked Peter to sell everything off, the only thing he had left was this grandiose yacht named *No Regrets*.

Peter reached the ramp leading up to the yacht, he gripped the metal railing, his knuckles turning white from the effort. His knees felt like jelly and his breathing was shallow. As he watched the gleaming white boat before him, bobbing gently in the dark water, he suddenly felt sick. Peter rarely got sea sick, but he guessed there was more to it than that. Swallowing thickly, he looked down at the package in his hand. It was a small picture frame that contained a picture of him, Emily, Alex and his first wife toasting their first big sale for the company. It was taken at the moment they knew they were going to be successful. Beneath the picture was their favorite ancient Chinese Proverb, *"The journey is the reward."*

Peter shook his head. A small breeze lifted off the water and as it brushed against his cheek he realized that it was wet. He wished he could have blamed the moisture running down his face to the spray of the sea, but as he quickly rubbed his hand across his face, he wished he could rub away the tightness in his chest as well. With the words of that quote bouncing around in his thoughts, he wondered. Why had they not seen what was before them? Did they honestly think that end of the journey really was the reward? How misguided they were! Alex lost an amazing woman and was never able to be vulnerable enough to fall in love again. To make matters worse, he nearly lost his relationship with his children in the process of letting the business consume him. Peter was following in his footsteps and Amanda looked like she was also well on her way to the same destructive path. Funny how no one thinks that being a devoted and successful business owner can also be so damaging to the rest of one's life, nearly like a drug. But, as the proverb reminded Peter in this moment, and he wished they had seen it sooner, was that being present and enjoying the journey filled with those around you was the source of true happiness. If he would have just stopped and taken notice, he would have indeed realized that the journey, each and every day, was the reward.

Peter blinked the tears out of his eyes, knowing that Alex wouldn't want to see them. He turned, and took a few steps down the dock, then he turned again and walked halfway up the plank. He repeated this back and forth pacing for a few more moments as he deliberated. The boat seemed quiet before his entry, but he knew Alex's family was onboard with him, saying what was most likely their last goodbyes. Maybe he should leave them to it? No, he shook his head. This gift was important and he had something he wanted to say to Alex while he still could. Giving himself a mental kick, Peter made sure his face was dry and composed as he marched down the ramp to say goodbye to his best friend.

At first Peter was surprised at the absence of the boat's crew members that were usually buzzing around, maintaining the massive boat, but then he realized this was truly a private family affair.

He paused for a moment before opening the door to the grand salon, knowing that's where everyone was congregated. The sounds he heard on the other side of the door resembled the birthday party he was going to, not the sad farewell he was dreading. Pushing the door open, a mix of emotions ran through Peter. He was delighted to see so many familiar faces turn to smile at him as he walked through the door. Even though some were tear streaked like his were earlier, they all looked at peace. The most peaceful presence in the room, however was the one propped up on the hospital like bed in the center of the room. An IV snaked into Alex's thin arm and a breathing tube wrapped horizontally across his face and head. A huge grin lifted Alex's sallow cheeks the minute he saw his best friend.

"Peter!" You could tell he was trying to call across the room, but his voice barely carried. The huddle of bodies around Alex's bed shifted to make room for Peter. A young man Peter didn't recognize dragged another chair over to the side of Alex's bed. Amanda beamed at him, murmuring her thanks, as she shifted her chair over to make room for the addition. The young man responded with a swift peck on her cheek and a squeeze of her hand before he moved out of the way so Peter could sit.

"Peter, I'd like to introduce you to the newest member of the family! Or soon to be member that is," Alex announced, his grin getting wider.

Peter looked at the young man in surprise, then at Amanda and once more at Alex.

"Jonathan proposed." Amanda explained, her cheeks pink, as she lifted her hand to show off the ring. The light from a nearby lamp caught at the facets in the diamond sending sparkling glimmers to bounce off the back of the closest upholstered chair.

"Wow! Congratulations!" Peter leaned in to give Amanda a hug and shook Jonathan's hand. He wondered, though, as joyous as this announcement was how Amanda was going to manage married life with her busy work schedule. He had noticed that she had slowed down a little lately, and they had made some significant process in creating the systems necessary to help her live a balanced life, but there was a lot of work to be done. Managing a new marriage and a demanding career would be difficult to say the least.

As if his thoughts were written across his features, Alex answered Peter. "Pastor Davis is actually on his way here. The kids were nice enough to indulge me one last time and get married today so I could see. But, before he gets here, there are a few important matters I would like to discuss with you."

As if on cue, those who were sitting began to rise making excuses for tasks they needed to complete before the small wedding would take place. Eventually, everyone drifted away. Peter was surprised at the last person to leave. The petite woman must have been hiding behind one of the family members because Peter hadn't noticed her when she came in. He had noticed Peter's kids and many of the business acquaintances they had spoken to recently, but not once did he notice Alex's ex-wife and "the one that got away."

"Oh hey, Samantha. How's the gallery?"

Without looking up from her task of smoothing the hair off Alex's brow she bent down to place a tender kiss on his temple. "It's doing very well, thank you." Her voice was sad, but tinged with hope. Finally she met Peter's gaze and leaned in to give him a hug. "It's good to see you." She gave a small smile, squeezed Alex's hand and followed the rest of the group out of the room. She tilted her head down to allow her long hair to swing forward like a curtain to shield her face.

"It's good to see you too, Samantha." As Samantha walked out of the room, Peter turned wide eyes on Alex, "Wow, I never thought I'd see the two of you in the same room again!"

Alex smirked, "I know, I can't believe she has forgiven me for everything I've put her through. She is an amazing woman."

"So she just decided to come see you today?"

"No." Alex coughed and grimaced, obviously in pain. "I visited her gallery to gather info about leadership and problem solving with employees. Where do you think I got all of that great information on handling employee disputes and accountability?"

"Well," Peter shifted in his seat, fidgeting by picking at his slacks. "After dealing with you all of these years, she is definitely the right person to ask about that!" Alex tried not to laugh and coughed instead. "I'm glad to see you two made amends."

"I should've---but no," Alex shook his head, "this is not the time to think about regrets." With his free hand, that wasn't tangled in IV cords, he pushed himself up further in the bed. "I made a lot of mistakes, but there are so many things I am thankful for."

"The kids certainly look great, I haven't seen them in a while," Peter tried straightening Alex's pillows the best he could.

"I've actually seen them a lot more lately. Especially Amanda. I have some amazing kids you know? Despite their old man, they turned out great. I wish I could take the credit, but can't."

"You're their father, and a good one I might add" Peter protested.

"Yeah, but honestly the only thing I think I've contributed is 'what not to do'," admitted Alex. "Amber is going to run the charity I had you set-up, she's been working with non-profits for years and is ready to take the helm of her own ship."

Peter smiled at the pun, and leaned forward in anticipation of the answer to his next question, "But, what about Amanda? Is she going to be able to handle marriage and being CEO of Moss Global? It just seems like a lot, but I'm sure you've been talking to her about how to balance everything, right?"

"Well," Alex drawled, "Yes and no. I have been talking to her a lot about work life balance and have been very open about my mistakes and regrets in that area. I had to ask for her forgiveness and try to make up for lost time as much as possible. However the biggest gift I could give her was my blessing."

"For the wedding," Peter agreed. "Of course."

Alex's lips twitched as he tried to reign in a knowing smile, "Yes, for that, but you know being the CEO of Moss Global was never her dream?"

Peter pursed his lips in thought, "Really? But, she went to business school, was following in your footsteps, and I thought you were grooming her for the position because she wanted it."

"No," Alex shook his head, "not exactly. She finally came clean to me before I left for Detroit last spring and I felt awful for not seeing it sooner."

"What do you mean, before you left Detroit? That was almost a year ago."

"Yes, I know. She reminded me about how she was always doctoring up her baby dolls as a little girl and often brought home injured animals to fix up, too. Anytime anyone in the house was sick,

Amanda was the nurse and you couldn't keep her away, no matter what threats you made against the possibility of her own health." Alex smiled fondly at the memory. "I wasn't home or involved enough to notice that her true passion was as a caretaker. She was good at it too."

Alex visibly swallowed as he struggled with the emotions the past dredged up, "She told me last spring that she really wanted to go to nursing school, and I shot the idea down."

"Oh Alex," Peter patted his friend on the shoulder. "I didn't know."

Alex continued, "She was upset of course, but I insisted that if I was paying for her school that she was going into business. We had a fight, which I know everyone heard about through the grapevine, but it wasn't until after my diagnosis that I began to patch things up with her."

"So," Peter looked at his old friend incredulously, "You aren't handing the company over to Amanda?"

"Nope," Alex paused for a beat, looking his friend in the eyes before dropping the next bombshell on him. "I'm giving the company to you."

Peter's mouth fell open before he collected himself, "What? Really? But, all this time, I thought we were making changes so Amanda could take things over?"

"I'm sorry if I misled you my friend, but I needed to be sure that you could change, Peter. You were already too much like me in your work habits and lifestyle that I was afraid of what making you CEO would do. I didn't want you to end up like me, losing everything you hold dear just for a business. I love you and Emily too much for that."

Peter sighed, "I used to think working this hard for the business was the same as being a good husband and father because I was providing a future. It was like being addicted to gambling or something. I kept thinking to myself, someday all of this will pay off huge! But, I have definitely seen the alternative over the past six months."

"I'm glad. It's been a privilege to see you grow. You tirelessly worked on every project and suggestion I had without complaint or without seeking compensation. Not one time did you ask what was in it for you. You are a really special man Peter and you deserve this."

"I don't know what to say." Peter tried hard not to allow the tears that was forming in his eyes to fall down his cheek.

"Peter, you are ready for this. And from what I hear from Amanda, Carly, Brandy and others is that the entire company is ready for you to take them into the future."

"But without you?" Peter couldn't help but to let out the tears he was holding back as he was imagining taking on the new challenge without his best friend and partner.

"You know what my biggest regret was Peter?"

"No, what?

"Over the past 20 years we spent building this company, I kept believing that I had to sacrifice my life every day so I could one day be successful. My biggest regret is that I didn't realize how I had everything I needed to be happy right there in front of me. And all of the challenges and obstacles we faced to build this thing, it was an incredible ride and there is no one in the world that I would have rather gone on it with than you." Alex could barely get out the last few words.

Still crying, Peter laughed as he handed his friend the present he still had clutched in one hand as he wiped away the tears from his face with the other, "You're going to think this is ironic, then. Happy Birthday, old fart."

"Ha! What is it?" Alex slowly ripped the paper from a small frame. His eyes scanned the picture that was revealed and paused over the Chinese Proverb. 'The journey is the reward.' "Wow, if we only would have known. Those were great times, weren't they?"

"They were the best," both Alex and Peter paused in reflection of gratitude and sorrow.

"Oh, and I have one more gift for you," Alex smiled as he reached by his side to grab a pair of keys tied to an anchor key chain.

"Alex—uh, what is that?"

"Well, no self-respecting CEO can live without their own boat." Alex gestured to the expansive room they were in.

"Are you serious? But I don't know if—"

"You can afford it? Don't worry I've taken care of all that, but this boat does come with a few contingencies."

"Ah, now we're talking business!" Peter's eyes twinkled with excitement.

"If you are to accept this boat, you have to do so on three conditions."

"OK, I'm ready."

"One, each month the boat is to be used to reward employees—I mean associates--who deserve the recognition. I think we both now realize how important it is to keep motivating with carrots instead of sticks. The boat should be a constant reminder for you give back to those who give so much to you...something I should have been doing years ago."

"Well, that one is easy. What's number two?"

"Next, each month the boat is to be used to show our appreciation to your best customers and those key people who send the company referrals on a frequent basis. Without your loyal customers, your business will die. Sorry…no pun intended."

"Done! And three?"

"Three, and the most important…the boat is for you and the family to enjoy. And I'm not talking about once a year Pete!" Alex coughed several times in the excitement to make his point. "Please don't do what I did. Take time out with them before it's too late. Tell them you love them every day and live the rest of your life with no regrets. Do we have a deal?"

Peter looked around at the elaborate decorations, paintings and plush furniture in amazement that this could actually be happening. On one hand, he was about to get everything he wanted. But on the other, he couldn't help but think that he had to lose his dearest friend to make it all happen. "You drive a hard bargain Mr. Moss, but I think I can settle for that. I promise, I will never let you down."

"You never have my friend, you never have." Alex smiled as he raised and opened his arms out to the side.

Alex leaned down to embrace the frail body of his friend. "Don't go," he whispered. He suddenly felt foolish and a tad bit like a needy child. It was the ache in his heart for his friend that was still clinging on.

"Go where? I have a wedding to attend!"

Peter laughed through the tears streaming down his face and embraced his friend one last time.

Do what you love to do!

November 6 ✓

If you don't listen to anything else I've written for you, choose a career that you love! Be true to yourself. Trust me when I say, life is too short to spend time in a career that does not express your passion and love of life.

I know I haven't been a good father and I wasn't there for my children when they needed me most. But I hope, that through these letters, they will know and it is my sincere wish that you will not make the same mistake. It's not too late!

"It isn't success if it costs you the companionship and chumminess and love for your children. Very often, busy, wealthy men of momentous affairs discover too late that they have sacrificed the finest thing in life, the affection of their family."
B.C. Forbes

Tell someone you love that you love them.

PART 14
THE LESSON

*"At the end of our lives, we will not be judged
by how many diplomas we have received, how much
money we have made or how many great things we
have done. We will be judged by "I was hungry and
you gave me something to eat. I was naked and you
clothed me. I was homeless and you took me in."*

Mother Teresa

Peter walked off the boat several hours later full of peace, but with a heavy heart which was an odd combination he attempted to reconcile all the way back home. His day wasn't over. Emily and the kids were still at her mother's for the evening and Peter was glad he would have some quiet time to recover from the day's events. He still had one more task to complete.

As he was leaving and saying his last goodbyes, Alex reminded him of the wrapped box he gave him almost six months ago and asked him to open it. He had often wondered what could be so important in the box and why Alex had wanted him to wait until his last days before he could unmask its contents.

Peter cautiously pulled the package out from the top shelf of his closet where he had hidden it from the boys. He knew the allure of a wrapped package to a little one all too well.

By the time he returned to his home office desk, he saw that he had missed two calls from Amanda and a text that read, "He's gone." Peter sank into his black office chair, his palms pressed together in front of his mouth as his elbows leaned on his desk. He held his breath, waiting for the emotion to overtake him like the current of tide, but he felt nothing. He knew this was coming. Was that why he felt nothing? He checked Amanda's message again. The words just didn't seem real to him. The time displayed in white numbers at the top of his phone however, where real and they reminded him that he only had about an hour before his family was home.

Peter slowly tore the paper away from the box and opened the enclosed envelope. He had to read the letter a full five times before he gave up and lifted the lid of the box. Just like the message of Alex's death the letter was too surreal to believe, the contents of the box soon slammed him back to reality with a sudden ferocity. The cards, the countless pictures, and the thin Moleskin journals cobbled together to make one big one had fresh tears streaming down Peter's face as he gave in to his grief.

Most people have one or two pivotal days in their lives that they remember well. It can be a marriage, a birth, a death, or an achievement. I've been fortunate enough to have several. As the make-up artist dabs powder across my nose and cheeks to deflect the stage's bright lights, and my hairstylist rubs the tension out of my neck, I'm brought back to the first of my pivotal moments. It was the moment that, in fact, brought me to where I am today as I prepare to speak before the largest audience that has ever attended one of my motivational seminars.

I was sixteen, fall was setting in and I was far enough into my school semester to where it was no longer exciting or new, but rather boring in its predictability. I was in my garage, re-taping my skateboard with Daft Punk streaming in through my earbuds, when a white Range Rover pulled up and a middle aged man stepped out. My heart clenched every time a man of his age and build walked by. As he got closer and I turned my music off I realized, that this guy wasn't the same one I always kept an eye out for. My hope deflated, I had only seen a picture of the man in question once. It had fallen behind my mom's dresser, and I found it as I was helping her move the furniture in her room the year before. She never spoke of my dad and since the picture was of them and the date before I was born, I hoped it could be him. We had the same nose and smile, and our hair curled at the nape of our neck in the same crooked manner no barber could fix. Luckily there was also a first and last name on the back with the date and a simple Google search revealed the guy's identity. He was pretty well known, and surprisingly easy to contact. We agreed to meet at my favorite ice cream shop in my hometown of New Haven, but he never showed and after waiting for an hour I left. I refused his calls after that. There is only so much abandonment a sixteen year old boy could take.

But the man standing before me, shaking my hand and introducing himself as Peter Walker was definitely not my father. Mr. Walker didn't say much, didn't ask for my mom, and he didn't stay long either. He merely handed me a soft black leather box and a key to a safety deposit box which he said was a gift from someone that loved me very much. As he was walking back to his SUV, he turned, smiled at me and said, "You look just like him, you know?"

As he drove away, I just stood there in the driveway paralyzed by the event that just occurred. An overwhelming myriad of emotions came over me as started to realize I was about to have the answers to the many questions I had about the man who was never a father. Why didn't he want me? What made him walk away? Is he going to give me the chance to yell and punish him for what he had done to me and my mother? Why didn't he give me the chance to prove to him that I was worthy of his love? Did I really look that much like him as Mr. Walker had said?

I walked into my house, laid the box on the coffee table and sat in silence to visualize what would be in that box. Not wanting to be disappointed, I tried to convince myself that the contents of the box really didn't matter. What could be so special about something that was no bigger than a shoebox? What could be inside that would actually make up for all of the pain and suffering he had caused?

As I placed the box and its contents on my lap, I could smell him. The hair stood up on the back of my neck as I touched the box and could somehow feel him watching me. This was a special gift and even before I opened it to reveal its magnificent treasure, I knew how much he adored me.

The box was lined with cashmere and everything was neatly organized in its place. There were pictures of me playing sports and at parties that I had never seen. A birthday card for every year appropriately numbered was on top of what appeared to be stock certificates and other financial documents. Beneath it all was an old and beaten up journal with a letter bound on top addressed to me. As a sixteen year old kid who had nothing but anger and resentment towards his father, the endowment of financial wealth meant nothing...it was the words carefully chosen in his letter and the knowledge in the diary that would change my life forever.

June 6

Dearest Ryan, my son,

Words cannot adequately express my sorrow for not being a part of your life. I realize there is absolutely nothing I could say to make up for what I've done. All I can do is open up my heart, tell you the truth and pray that one day, you will forgive me. I would understand if you never did.

If you are reading this letter, it means that I have passed. I asked my best friend and business partner, Peter Walker to deliver this message to you and I trust that when you are ready, he will be there for you to answer your questions as I am sure there are hundreds you would like, and deserve to have answers to about me and the decisions I made in my life. I will do my best to provide some clarity and address a few of them now.

Your mother and I met when I was at a conference in San Diego a year before you were born. She was and still is an amazing woman. Our relationship lasted a little over 6-months and I truly believe they were some of the happiest times of my life. She fell in love fast and I could feel myself doing the same. Moss Global was growing faster than I had ever imagined and it took all I had to keep things headed in the right direction. I guess I could have slowed down, but the truth was, I was really not over my first failed marriage which had just occurred two years prior.

Your mother knew I was still in love with her and in love with my work. We were just in different places in our life and she wanted more from me than I was willing to give. I don't blame her for not telling me about you until a few weeks before your first birthday. I wanted so much to see you but honored her wishes to keep my distance.

Over the years, she kept me informed of what was going on in your life and I attended every birthday, baseball and soccer game that I could. I kept my distance, and even though she didn't say anything, I believe your mother caught me walking around a time or two. She still looks so beautiful. You have her eyes. Once, after a game you ran right by me. It took all I had not to grab you and hold on as long I could!

Peter and others at the office always wondered where I was going off to when I left to see you play. I already felt like the biggest failure in the world and telling them I had a son and was not part of his life was too much to handle.

It was so difficult seeing you on the field watching other children with their fathers in attendance. That must have been so difficult. I took pictures and hoped that one day, we could be together. One day led to another and before I knew it, you were all grown-up.

I couldn't believe it when your mother contacted me to let me know you had found a picture of us and wanted to meet. I had a conference to attend in Detroit and was going to fly out to see you the same day. It was that day I collapsed on stage and later found out about the cancer. Son, no one knew I was going to see you and could notify you or your mother about what had happened. When you wouldn't return my calls, I realized it was too late and I was getting what I had deserved.

All I want you to know is that my absence doesn't in anyway mean that I don't love you with my whole heart. I am so proud of the young man you have become. Your mother tells me about how well you have done in school and how you help her around the house. I only wish I could have seen the great things I'm certain you will accomplish in your life.

I know I don't deserve to give you advice or tell you what to do. But I do want to give you a gift that is very special to me. In the box with this letter, you will find a diary where I have logged the past 20 years of my life. Please keep it and refer to it often. More than about business, it's about life. You see, most people who try and live the American Dream and start a business have no idea what they are getting into. God knows Peter and I had no idea what was ahead of us!

Please pay particular attention to the last 6-months in the journal. Unfortunately, it wasn't until after my diagnosis that things become clear to me about how life should have been. Had I known 20 years ago what I had known then, things would have been completely different. I would have continued to build Moss Global and work long hours, but the way in which I would have done it would have been drastically different. I also would have begged and pleaded with your mother to allow me to be in your life — regardless if we were ever married or not.

If you do decide to venture out on your own, always understand that at the end of the day, it's not a better business you are trying to create — it's a better life! If you follow the guidelines and principles I've written out, you will not make the mistakes that Peter and I did long ago. Building a business can give you the flexibility, freedom and feeling of accomplishment like no other career. But if you do it wrong, it can destroy your life.

And finally, cherish every day that God has blessed you with. I'm certain that if you look hard, happiness and success *is all around you now without you even knowing it. It is my final prayer and desire that you take the time learn from my mistakes and are truly happy. If you are, then my life and sacrifice was worth it and that is the best gift I can give to you.*

I love you always,

Dad

That letter was a lot to take in, and shifting through that box of memories and flipping through the pages of his journal was even more mind boggling. Not long after opening that box, my mother showed me more pictures and told me all the gifts he had given me over my life. He had taken care of her financially and left me a large inheritance which was set-up in his estate. However, it wasn't the gifts or the money that I needed from him. It was the one phrase from his letter that I needed more than anything. "I love you very much." That's all I really needed to know.

As I stand here in the wings of the same conference center my father met my mother, listening to the buzz of the audience as they wait for me to enter the stage, I'm not going to lie to you. It took me several months and many heated arguments with my mother before I was able to process the situation. As much as I wanted to hate my father even more, his profession of love made it hard for me to do so.

Then I read his journal. As a sixteen year old the business side of things held little interest. It was his personal life that was the most intriguing. I made it a habit of reading the book once a year on the same day, as though celebrating an anniversary. By the time I turned twenty-one, the business concepts laid out in the journal began to make more sense and helped me in more ways that I could image.

It was clear from the language he used that my dad thought of himself as a failure. Sure he made a lot of money, knew famous and powerful people, and was the CEO of a highly sought after company. But, the very last journal entries, the ones he wrote in his last six months was full of pain and regret. He missed out on many of life's beautiful moments because his head was stuck in the sand that was his business. It took a cancer diagnosis to see the light. That light was bright enough to reveal the darker side of his life that he had never wanted to acknowledge, but acknowledge it he did. Through his claim of responsibility he taught me the biggest lesson of my life. Be present and enjoy what you have now.

I know many of you who have heard my tale either own a business that you are a slave to, or are thinking about going into business for yourself. Wherever you are on the journey, just know that it is never too late. You don't know how much time you have left on this earth, but every breath you take and every action you fulfill has a ripple effect on the lives of those around you. Wake up and pay attention! You don't want to someday realize that all of the time and devotion you gave to your business should have been relished on your loved ones, friends, community and your health. Your business should work for you, from day one, not the other way around. The goal is not to get to the point where your business works for you, the goal is to start the business that way.

If my father had not taught me how to live a fulfilling and happy life of no regrets while also being a successful businessman, I wouldn't be where I am today. I've been happily married for eighteen years, am the proud father of three children, and am about to experience another pinnacle of my career. There is a large stadium of people out there who bought tickets to my business coaching conference and have waited months to hear what I have to say. My entire family including my two half-sisters, their husbands and total of 5 children are in the front row. After this event, we are using an account our father had set-up for the three of us that we found out about during the reading of his estate. He gave us the money with one condition – we had to use it for pleasure travel only when we all three could be together with our families. Even from his grave he is a bit of a control freak!

Alex Moss may have thought of himself as a failure, but if he was a failure, he had to have been The Most Successful Failure in the World!

ACKNOWLEDGEMENTS

As I sit down now to write this, I can't help but remember how many people have either influenced the writing or contributed to the ideas presented in this book. And to some, this section would be more appropriately titled an "Apology" rather than "Acknowledgements". First and foremost, I acknowledge the sacrifice that my family made during the course of journey to enlightenment. Kristin, Avery and Logan, I love you to the moon and back.

Next, I owe a debt of gratitude to my extended family at Farmers Insurance. There are too many to mention, but special thanks to the 60 agents and almost 200 support staff of district 65, I miss you very much. To Megan LaFollett, Ella Hearrean and Ida Jansson at Chart House Press, thank you for all of your hard work and support to make this happen on time and under budget.

To my assistant writer and friend Carly Drake, who listened to my story and brought life to the characters we portrayed. She encouraged me to be open and honest throughout the writing of this book in the most difficult times, without judgment or contempt, so that we may help others who are struggling with similar difficulties.

And finally, to all my readers, clients, employees and contractors who continue to support our important work at the Jeff Hastings Agency and Chart House Press.

Thank you all.

CPSIA information can be obtained
at www.ICGtesting.com
Printed in the USA
FSOW01n2209290815
10329FS